Nation First

Essays in the Politics of Ancient Indian Studies

(Including an Analysis of the CAG Rep
on the Archaeological Survey of India

Nation First

Essays in the Politics of Ancient Indian Studies

(Including an Analysis of the CAG Report on the Archaeological Survey of India)

Dilip K. Chakrabarti

Aryan Books International
New Delhi

Nation First: Essays in the Politics of Ancient Indian Studies

ISBN: 978-81-7305-526-3

Disclaimer: The views and contents of the book are solely of the author. The publisher may not subscribe to them.

First Published: 2014

Reprinted in **2017** by:

Aryan Books International

Pooja Apartments, 4B, Ansari Road, New Delhi-110 002 (India)

Tel.: 23287589, 23255799; Fax: 91-11-23270385

E-mail: aryanbooks@gmail.com

www.aryanbooks.co.in

Designed and Printed in India at

ABI Prints & Publishing Co., New Delhi

For

Shri Y. Krishan, and his daughter
Kalpana Krishan Tadikonda,
in grateful acknowledgement of their support in
Delhi University in 1985 and later

Preface

While trying to explain the philosophy of the Vivekananda International Foundation, of which he is a Distinguished Fellow, to a seminar audience, Lt.General (retired) R. K. Sawhney, PVSM, AVSM, who is also a former Deputy Chief of Army Staff and a former Director General of Military Intelligence, put it simply as 'nation first'. As an ordinary academic present in that audience, I was somewhat taken aback and certainly deeply touched because in all my years in the Indian academia associated with ancient Indian history and archaeology, I never heard the nation being mentioned in the context of our discipline.

When one considers the issue in some depth one realizes that it should not be a matter of surprise at all, nor is it a matter of recent development. Even those Indian historians who were dubbed nationalists by some of their successors allowed themselves to be dominated entirely by the general frame of thought which was popularized by Western historians vis-à-vis India. They might have been critical of a few specific ideas but beyond them they did not proceed. The ancient historians who succeeded them as a group were, regrettably, a lot inferior to their predecessors in the sense that they did not bother too much about acquiring a detailed expertise in the primary source materials. They tried to make up for this by thinking of various social science categories and trying to relate them to the data in hand without looking closely at whether these categories satisfactorily fitted the data. For instance, the frame of 'lineage to state', as applied to the ancient Indian context by one of these historians, seems to be intellectually satisfying on the surface but when one thinks of some of the basic imponderables of the relevant sources (i.e. the corpus of the Vedic literature) such as the absence of a rigorous internal chronology and the general dubiousness of many of the cultural assumptions regarding them, one realizes that the frame offered does not take us to a higher level of perception regarding ancient India.

The general lack and impreciseness of the vast bulk of our ancient Indian sources cannot be denied. A logically arranged and reasonably detailed 'people's history' of ancient India is very much a wishful thinking on the basis of the available sources, and one could try to get around this by focussing on ground investigations of various kinds. The process has possibly just begun but still there is a very long way to go.

Archaeology should have played a leading role in bringing about this change. Regrettably the theoretical frames of our archaeologists of the post-Independence era did not allow any scope of originality to the land. They tried to make discoveries but their thought- pattern was dominated wholly by the colonial masters who had just left. I suppose it was only in the area of making discoveries that they were displaying some concern for enriching the past of the country.

The fact that nation plays no part at all in an average Indian archaeologist's imagination is clear from the simple fact that most of the archaeological research done in the country remains unpublished. The level of literacy has also come down significantly in this area because very few of us are familiar these days with the general situation of the subject in various fields in the country.

The lack of any national concern is also manifest in the way in which collaboration with foreign archaeological groups has become a sought-after agenda on the part of many Indian nationally funded universities and other institutions. International collaboration in the field of the nation's heritage is not a bad thing in itself, as long as there is a sense of respect for the country's knowledge tradition in the subject on the part of the international collaborators. J.D. Clark of Berkeley ran a fruitful collaborative programme with G.R. Sharma of Allahabad. In the case of Pakistan, the British museum established a fruitful collaborative programme with Pakistani archaeologists in Bannu. In Pakistan, again, the French set up a long-standing excavation programme in Baluchistan. In India, things have been different mainly because the Indian collaborators have been remarkably deficient in putting their own cases forward, provided they had any case to forward at all. In each case without exception, the cases of foreign archaeological collaboration in India have been dependent exclusively on the principal foreign collaborator's money and ideas. The so-called 'joint publications' in these cases are mostly written by the principal foreign collaborator who in order to make his/her path smooth offers various kinds of personal incentives to the concerned Indians. He/she is not concerned with what effect his/her writings will have on the Indians' perception of the cultural heritage or history of their country. He/she has already taken care of this issue by offering bribes of different kinds to the participating Indians. With the passing away of people like Peter Ucko and Bruce Trigger, the number of people who are basically respectful to the knowledge tradition of the Third World are also fast disappearing in international archaeology, and in their place we have people who are so full of themselves that they should not be let in the archaeology of the Third World areas like India.

However unpleasant the foregoing may sound, this unfortunately is the reality, and the Indian archaeologists, if they want to serve the nation in any way, should be mindful of this reality and play their own parts in changing the situation. The essays and notes of the present volume have tried to throw light on the harsh reality of this situation in various ways. Many of these essays and notes have been published in various scattered places, and one hopes that their publication in a compact form will highlight the issues they have been concerned with.

Contents

By the Same Author

AUTHORED BOOKS

1. *The Antiquities of Kangra* (with S.J. Hasan): Delhi 1984: Munshiram Manoharlal.
2. *A History of Indian Archaeology from the Beginning to 1947*. Delhi 1988: Munshiram Manoharlal.
3. *Theoretical Issues in Indian Archaeology*. Delhi 1988: Munshiram Manoharlal.
4. *The External Trade of the Indus Civilization*. Delhi 1990: Munshiram Manoharlal.
5. *Ancient Bangladesh, a Study of the Archaeological Sources*. Delhi 1992: OUP.
6. *The Early Use of Iron in India*. Delhi 1992: OUP.
7. *Archaeology of Eastern India: Chhotanagpur Plateau and West Bengal*. Delhi 1993: Munshiram Manoharlal.
8. *The Archaeology of Ancient Indian Cities*. Delhi 1995: OUP.
9. *Copper and Its Alloys in Ancient India* (with Nayanjot Lahiri). Delhi 1996: Munshiram Manoharlal.
10. *Colonial Indology: Sociopolitics of the Ancient Indian Past*. Delhi 1997: Munshiram Manoharlal.

11. *The Issues in East Indian Archaeology*. Delhi 1998: Munshiram Manoharlal.
12. *Bharatvarsher Pragitihas* (in Bengali). Kolkata 1999: Ananda Publishers.
13. *India—An Archaeological History*. Delhi 1999: OUP.
14. *Archaeological Geography of the Ganga Plain: The Lower and the Middle Ganga*. Delhi 2001: Permanent Black.
15. *Archaeology in the Third World: A History of Indian Archaeology since 1947*. Delhi 2003: Munshiram Manoharlal.
16. *The Archaeology of European Expansion in India, Gujarat, c. 16th-18th Centuries*. Delhi 2003: Aryan Books.
17. *The Archaeology of the Deccan Routes, the Routes which Linked the Ganga Plain with the Deccan*: Delhi 2005: Munshiram Manoharlal.
18. *The Oxford Companion to Indian Archaeology*. Delhi 2006: OUP.
19. *Archaeological Geography of the Ganga Plain: Upper Ganga (Oudh, Rohilkhand and the Doab)*. Delhi 2007: Munshiram Manoharlal.
20. *The Battle for Ancient India: An Essay in the Socio-Politics of Indian Archaeology*. Delhi 2008: Aryan Books.
21. *Globalization and Indian Archaeology, and Other Essays*. Banaras 2009: Banaras Hindu University.
22. *The Problem of the Sarasvati River and Notes on the Archaeological Geography of Haryana and Indian Panjab* (with Sukhdev Saini). Delhi 2009: Aryan Books.
23. *The Ancient Routes of the Deccan and the Southern Peninsula*. Delhi 2010: Aryan Books.

24. *The Geopolitical Orbits of Ancient India, the Geographical Frames of the Ancient Indian Dynasties*. Delhi 2010: OUP.
25. Royal Messages by the Wayside: Historical Geography of the Asokan Edicts. Delhi, 2011: Aryan Books.
26. *Fifty Years of Indian Archaeology (1960-2010): Journey of a Foot Soldier*. Delhi 2012: Aryan Books.

EDITED BOOKS

1. *Essays in Indian Protohistory* (coeditor D.P. Agrawal). Delhi 1979: B.R. Publishing.
2. *A Source-Book of Indian Archaeology* (co-editor F.R. Allchin), 3 volumes (Delhi 1979, 1997, 2003): Munshiram Manoharlal.
3. *Indus Civilization Sites in India: New Discoveries*. Mumbai 2004: Marg Publications.
4. *History of Ancient India*, Vols. 1 to 5, Delhi 2014: Vivekananda International Foundation & Aryan Books International.

1

Introduction

Does Nation Matter in the Current Ancient Historical and Archaeological Studies in India?

In this 'introduction' I propose to draw attention to two things. First, with reference to a recent publication by a well-recognized historian of ancient India, I shall show that the very term 'nationalism' is used by her in a pejorative sense. Secondly, moving closer to my own scene, i.e. Indian archaeology, I shall show how Indian archaeology is increasingly being tied to the apron-strings of fairly unscrupulous and pompous First World archaeologists in the name of international collaboration and recognition. There is no point in blaming the concerned First World ladies and gentlemen—a good number of them these days are plain racist louts anyway—but our own brethren keen on cadging all-expenses-paid international visits out of their collaborators should carefully consider the question of whose interests they eventually serve in the process.

DENIGRATION OF NATIONALISM IN THE STUDY OF ANCIENT INDIA: A CASE STUDY OF ROMILA THAPAR'S LAWRENCE DANA PINKHAM MEMORIAL LECTURE, 2012

'Nationalism' or a 'nationalist approach to history' has long been used by and large in a pejorative sense by modern India's historians, especially those who became powerful in the wake of the establishment of Indian Council of Historical Research in the early 1970s. To draw attention to the fact that this attitude to the nationalist Indian historians still persists, one can do no better than cite Romila Thapar's "Lawrence Dana Pinkham Memorial Lecture" in Chennai in May 2012. Thapar, who was a prominent member of the coterie of historians associated with the Indian Council of Historical Research, has long been a *Prima Donna* of ancient Indian studies both in India and the West, and her admirers go into tantrums at any kind of criticism of her, as they apparently did when her selection as a recipient of the Kleuge prize was questioned by some Americans of Indian origin. She has not done much empirical research but considerably embellished her writings with smooth references to different vignettes of social science literature and suggestions on how they should be incorporated in the study of ancient India. This is the kind of history which is liked by a vast section of India's English-educated 'progressive' middle class and their intellectual parents in the different 'Indian studies' establishments of the Western academia who marvel at the sight of this Third World woman who speaks their academic language, knows the etiquette and style of their 'senior common rooms' and is competent enough to express their ideas with supreme ease and confidence.

The second paragraph of this lecture on 'reporting history: early India' begins with an imagined dichotomy between 'British colonial historians' and 'nationalist historians'. *I do not find the idea of such a dichotomy acceptable in the light of the empirical evidence.* For instance, there is no attitudinal difference to Indian history and culture between the 'British colonialist historian' E.J. Rapson, the Cambridge Sanskritist who was the editor of the *Cambridge History of India*, Vol. I, *Ancient India,* (1922) and the Deccan College archaeological *guru* H.D. Sankalia (1973). Rapson wrote in 1922 that "the migrations and the conquests which provided human energy" with which the Indian civilizations were created had "invariably come into India from the outside". In 1973, in an article in *World Archaeology,* Sankalia expressed exactly the same sentiment. According to him the sun of civilization for India had always risen in the West. Examples of this kind may be multiplied *ad finitum* and underline the unpleasant fact that the basic structural premises of ancient Indian history as formulated in the colonial context continued unchanged till the recent period.

Regarding the notion of race, which Thapar mentions early in this lecture, it may be mentioned that, however unacceptable this may be in the modern context, the idea of a historical correlation between race, language and history was accepted unquestioned by India's ancient historians including Thapar who, in some of her early publications, identifies the Aryans as a distinct group of people speaking a distinct language and bringing horses to India. In an earlier context, R.C. Majumdar not merely accepted the idea in its entirety but also extended it to southeast Asia where the role which was suggested for the Aryans in India went to the Indian immigrants in that region. It is an unfortunate fact and a poor reflection on the way history is taught in India that the race concept is still a potent force in the perception of the Indian middle class. Those who dispute this statement may well consider the fact that fellow-Indians from the north-eastern parts of the country are frequently harassed in our capital on the ground that they look different. Is this situation less reprehensible than the communalism which our 'secular' historians and archaeologists vociferously condemn and against which they are known to have undertaken *Dharnas*? Is racism less reprehensible than communalism in the eyes of these scholars?

The people who have been dubbed 'nationalist historians' by scholars like Thapar questioned only the peripherals of the historical assumptions of the colonial period. Yet, people like Majumdar in their own ways tried to add something to the national pride. If some of them argued for the prevalence of a democratic system in the early republics or questioned the importance of Alexander's invasion or the presence of Indo-Greeks in India, they should be given unqualified credit for what they tried to do. In retrospect, they were not powerful enough or even astute enough to question the general frame of historical explanations they inherited from their rulers, and to be fair to them, that frame has been left in place by the historians who came to power in independent India with full government patronage in the early 1970s.

If that frame came in for criticism from any quarter, that came from a few great students of Indian affairs: for example, Gandhi who does not seem to use the term 'Aryan' anywhere in his writings; Vivekananda who was no historian but nonetheless realized that the whole Aryan idea was foisted on the Indians by Western scholars; Ambedkar whose legal mind perceived that there was no logic behind this idea; Rabindranath who regretted that the history of India, as taught to us, brought about a sense of separation between the land and its people. None of the ideas of these true nationalists ever got into the history books written by scholars like Majumdar or Thapar. The so-called nationalist historians or the self-styled enlightened ones had no difficulty in accepting the basic overarching frame of ancient India as laid down by the old colonial historians. In fact, there should not be any logical distinction between the colonial historians and many of their successors. What difference is there between what Rapson thought and what Sankalia thought, although their writings were well separated in time?

Those familiar with the archaeological issues throughout the 1950s, 1960s and 1970s will know that virtually all aspects of Indian archaeological issues were dominated, except some rare exceptions, by what old colonial scholars like D.H. Gordon and Mortimer Wheeler thought. Archaeological research no doubt expanded during this period but the mindset of the Indian scholarship during this period was basically a continuation of the old colonial mindset. Did Thapar herself question any entrenched colonial idea of Indian history in her Penguin version of the history of ancient India? Her distinction between the colonial and nationalist historians is unacceptable. Whether it is Rapson or Sankalia, or Vincent Smith and Romila Thapar, they all are colonialists, if we simply look at the continuity of ideas between their periods.

In fact, the only approach which could bring about a complete change in our perception of Indian history was what may be called an essentially archaeological approach to relate this history to the land. Except some limited attempts on the basis of limited resources, this approach has not witnessed even a proper beginning in modern India, and the fact that archaeological studies on the basis of which the Indian land mass may assume a distinct historical reality have not even significantly caught on in modern

India is an ample indication of how pointless is the general range of historical quibbles emanating from historians like Thapar.

The question of periodisation of ancient Indian history, which Thapar writes about, is hardly a matter of great significance, with all the terms currently in use having some logic and relevance. I think that Thapar's idea that "ancient India was projected as a virtual utopia" is untrue and has to be ignored unless accompanied by specific historiographical research. No professional historian of ancient India, Majumdar and K.P. Jayaswal included, ever projected ancient India as a utopia.

Personally I find Thapar's reluctance to consider religion as a historical factor in India rather surprising, especially in view of the fact that the cataclysmic event of Partition took place in the name of religion. She writes that the religion of the Harappans is unknown. This is certainly not the case, although I would not put a modern name to it. I would not call it a version of modern Hinduism but a lot of the elements which later became important parts of Hinduism were there. What is the basic problem in accepting this simple proposition which has been staring archaeologically at us for a long time? What is the virtue in championing the claim that the induction of what has been called the Indo-Aryan language family is post-Indus civilization on the basis of a completely unstable Rigvedic chronology? Is there any way by which the *Rigveda* can be dated to anybody's satisfaction? What is the reason of showing undue deference to what the comparative philologists write about the language history of India? There is no reason why archaeology should give a toss about this because linguistic reconstructions and their assumed chronology stand entirely on their own, without any independent support for their historicity.

To come back to the issue of periodisation of Indian history, there cannot be any single answer, nor is such an answer particularly necessary. One need not feel terrified at the prospect of lumping the whole period up to *c.* AD 1200 as 'ancient'; after all, it is the history of only 2000 years, assuming that historical writing began about 800 BC. If one feels happy by coining a separate phrase called 'early mediaeval' for the post-Gupta period till the coming of the Muslims, one is entitled to do so. Let us, however, not claim that this is based on detailed studies of socio-economic changes during this period. The concepts of 'feudalism', urban decay and an evanescent trade and commerce during this period, although much trumpeted by a particular section of ancient historians, may turn out to be fairly shaky on detailed research. In Europe itself there is no single idea of feudalism, and the less said about the idea of missing cities and trade and commerce in India during this period the better. In any case, the term 'early mediaeval' for the post-Gupta period is unlikely to harm anybody as long as one remembers that it is nothing but a term to describe the post-Gupta context. There need not be any objection to the use of the terms Hindu, Muslim and British either, because, for one thing the historical sources get written primarily in the non-Indian languages of Arabic and Farsi in the Muslim period and in English during the rule of the British.

Thapar's attempt to paint herself and others of her ilk martyrs in the cause of historical studies is downright amusing:

> Ancient India was projected as a virtual utopia, starting with the Vedic age and culminating 1500 years later in the so-called "golden age" of the Guptas. It was supposedly a period of unchanging prosperity. Society functioned according to the norms laid down in the *Shastras*, so historians did not have to investigate the reality.

> But let me add that this was not a situation typical of India alone. All nationalisms have to have a utopian past, preferably located as far back in time as possible. With limited evidence the imagination is free to conjure up a romantic past. Questioning this ideal picture is treated as an anti-national act, as it happened in India not so long ago. Some of us have been subjected to the slings and arrows of extreme religious nationalist views when we have tried to give a more integrated and reality-based view of the past. Historians began to analyse early Indian society in the 1960s and 1970s to arrive at a more realistic picture. But the opposition to this research was articulated through a range of religious organizations whose main concern was using religion for political mobilisation and for acquiring authority. This has now increased and has become more recognizable.

Thapar would not possibly know much about the history of Indian art. She would otherwise have known that the Gupta period symbolises everything that is best in Indian art tradition and is the culmination of a long period of development. This period certainly represented a golden age of Indian art and by implication, a golden phase of India's historic development as well. There is nothing *Prima facie* objectionable to this idea. If Thapar had taken care to tabulate the specific points which have been developed by her and others of her group for a 'more integrated and reality-based view of the past', we would have been in a better position to appreciate her arguments.

She also seems to be upset about attempts to use "religion for political mobilisation and for acquiring authority". Such attempts, especially if they have led to the loss of human lives, are surely unfortunate and have to be condemned, but are such attempts unknown even in the comparatively recent past of the subcontinent? Was not the entire Pakistan movement based on the Islamic identity of its protagonists? Are the attempts of some modern Indian politicians to introduce a religion-based quota system for jobs, etc. any less reprehensible?

When Thapar writes about being "subjected to the slings and arrows of extreme religious nationalist views", one cannot help but feel amused. As usual, the specific details are missing, but the only thing which others could observe was that with the coming of the NDA government at the centre, she and others of her group lost their importance in the power grouping of the government-sponsored Indian Council of Historical Research. Considering that she and others of her historical group were at the helm of the country's historical affairs since the early 1970s, this loss of power in the government has to be counted as a normal professional hazard which the historians closely tied to the strings of political power of the country like Thapar should take easily in her strides. On the contrary, they should feel very satisfied that for a long uninterrupted stretch since the take-over of the financial and other powers of Indian historical research by their group, they enjoyed the role of a kind of divine pantheon in the firmament of Indian historical studies.

A significant part of Thapar's essay tries to gloss over the harshness of the Islamic conquest of India. Such attempts are pointless. As is well known, Islam has not always been kind to 'infidels', and there is absolutely no reason to suggest otherwise, as Thapar does. However, the modern relation between Islam and the infidels in modern India must not be judged by what happened during the Islamic conquest of the land. If she considers that some historians have judged the methods and impact of the Islamic conquest of India harshly without any solid historical reason, she is welcome to write about it in detail, but to be honest, any apology for the conquest is unnecessary.

Her pontification of the civilizations being products of the intermingling of cultures is unnecessary. What she wilfully ignores is the silliness of attempts to explain the basic style and form of a civilization, old or new, in terms of diffusions from elsewhere. In the case of India this unfortunately has been the unchallenged assumption since the middle of the nineteenth century, and this is precisely what has been challenged since the 1970s. May we remind Thapar that a Ph.D. thesis on the Indus trade done under her supervision in the late 1960s or early 1970s argued that the role of the Indus Civilization was that of a supplier of raw materials to the contemporary Mesoptamia. In a review of the published form of this dissertation in *Puratattva,* I pointed out that there was a clear similarity between the author's opinion of the position held by the Indus Civilization in relation to Mesopotamia and the position of colonial India in relation to Britain. There is a steady continuity between the historical approaches of scholars like Rapson, Sankalia and other scholars of ancient India in modern India, including Thapar and her kind. There is no sense of national pride in the intellectual horizon of these historians.

Thapar should realize that languages are always in a state of flux, being subject not merely to cultural intermingling but also to the various nuances of class and cultural background subject in their turn to socio-economic factors of various kinds. But to be used satisfactorily for historical analysis, we have to realize that language studies do not have any chronological parameter of their own and thus whatever one may say about the correlation of language and a particular archaeological stratum devoid of writing is subjective, and not bound by any independent verification. In fact, trying to combine language with non-literate archaeological groups has been a breeding ground of various ethnic and eventually racist hypotheses in archaeology. Modern First World archaeologists are not unduly bothered by this because the issue of ethnicity does not cause bloodshed in their societies but the Third World situation is different and Third World archaeologists need not get involved in shady hypotheses with ethnic implications.

I am glad that Thapar has eventually admitted that "so far we have no archaeological evidence to prove an invasion by an Aryan race". I write 'eventually' because it is easy to demonstrate with reference to many early writings of Thapar that she was very much a believer in the coming of the Aryans as a group of people bringing in horses. However, in the same breath she writes that the

> picture is complicated, because we also do not have the evidence that the language—Old Indo-Aryan/Vedic Sanskrit—was spoken in India prior to 1500 BC. Since this is later than the Harappan cities, the Harappans were not Aryan-speaking. Nor do we know the language spoken by the Harappans. However languages related to Indo-Aryan were used in two areas. One was Old Iranian—the language of the Zorastrians and their text called *Avesta*—used in northeast Iran and the other was the language of the Hittites in northern Syria.

Apart from the opinion that the language of the Harappans is still unknown, everything mentioned in the above-mentioned propositions is liable to questionings.

The Avestan literature evolved over a long length of time, some of it attributable to the historical periods of the Achaemenids (6th century BC) and the Parthians (3rd century BC to 3rd century AD). The core of the *Avesta* has been put towards the end of the second millennium BC, but Zarathushtra has also been dated as late as the 7th century BC. There is no doubt a strong element of similarity between the Rigvedic and the Avestan languages, as various historians of the Sanskrit language argue, but whether this implies a similar chronological point cannot be said. The geography of the Avestan literature supposedly extends from Seistan to Merv but is also said to be focused in the central Afghanistan highlands. This geographical orbit was very familiar to the Indus Civilization, and the persistence of an Indian language tradition was quite possible in this orbit, whatever might have been the basic language of this civilization. The point is that the similarity in the language between the *Avesta* and the *Rigveda* cannot be translated in terms of the date of the *Rigveda* nor can this be interpreted as a springboard of the migration of the Indo-Iranian language family to India.

The second issue of 'the language of the Hittites in north Syria' is equally problematic and has been expressed clearly by P. Thiemme in his article "the 'Aryan' gods of the Mitanni treaties" in 1960 in *Journal of the American Oriental Society* 80 (4): 301-17.

What emerges on the whole is the presence of a few Sanskritic deities and words in the old Hittite territory or modern Anatolia in about 1400 BC, with margins on either side. The similarity lies only in a few Sanskrit-sounding words in both the Kikkuli horse-training text of *c.* 1400 BC and the treaty between Suppiluliuma, the Hittite king of *c.* 1380–1345 BC and Mattiwaza, the Mitanni (southeast Anatolia and northern Syria) king of the period. The mention of the Rigvedic gods *Mitra*, *Varuna*, *Indra* and the two *Nasatyas* occurs – it may be noted—*as a part of a rather long list of non-Rigvedic gods and goddesses.*

Whether such similarities in words mark the route of the Indo-European language-speakers to the subcontinent or mark their route out of it is a point which cannot be decided either way. Philological research does not have any historical marker, nor an earlier piece of this kind of philological research automatically gets superseded by newer versions. However, the fact of the presence of Indian words in West Asia may not be as mysterious as it sounds. The Indus seals are known to occur in the Kassite context in Mesopotamia and the Gulf, showing that this civilization remained in contact with West Asia as late as the 14th century BC. The beginning of this contact is dated as early as the Royal Graves of Ur of *c.* 2600 BC. Whatever might be the language or languages of the Indus Civilization, it was clearly a contact of more than a thousand years between India and West Asia. If one remembers this simple point, one does not have to be surprised by the presence of admittedly few Indian words in some West Asiatic documents. In the case of the *Avesta*, it may be noted that the core area of its geography from southeastern Iran to the southern Central Asia lies very much within the general orbit of contacts of the Indus Civilization. Further, the location of the site of Shortughai in the Kokcha Valley north of the Hindukush leaves no doubt about the pre-eminence of the role of the Indus Civilization in this region. Thus, to try to support the overarching frame of Aryan origins and migration from Europe to India with the help of the presence of a few Indian-sounding words in some 14th century West Asiatic documents does not seem to be a valid or logical exercise. It is time Thapar and her kind appreciated the rationale behind this argument.

One is somewhat amused by Thapar's observation that the Rigvedic people "were cattle-herders looking for good pastures" and that "they settled wherever ecology was suitable". People all through history settled wherever they thought that the ecology was suitable; so, that is not the point. The point is whether the main basis of the Rigvedic economy was primarily cattle-herding. That it included plough agriculture as well is clear from *RV*.III.57: "May the ploughshares break up our land happily; may the ploughman go happily with the oxen; may Parjanya water the earth with sweet showers happily".

In 1988 Tuk Tuk Kumar published her Ph.D. dissertation under my guidance in Delhi University Department of History as a book, *History of Rice in India*. The book contains clear references to the Rigvedic familiarity with agriculture and also to the probability that rice was known to the authors of the *Rigveda*. When I pointed out this to R.S. Sharma, he replied that all these Rigvedic references were later insertions—*prakshiptas*. His mind, like that of Thapar, was already made up regarding the *Rigveda* being primarily a cattle-herders' book. The veracity of anything which argues against it must be denied.

Thapar also thinks that "we should get away from meaningless questions like, whether the Aryan-speakers were indigenous to India". When Indians have been subjected, for more than a hundred years, to the opinion that the Aryan-speakers came to India from outside and laid the basis of the Indian religion of Hinduism and when Thapar's fellow-travellers like R.S.Sharma write books like *Advent of the Aryans in India,* the question cannot be as meaningless or innocuous as Thapar makes it sound. In her dictionary "the question of indigenous and foreign" may be a "non-question" but this has framed the Indians' perception of themselves for a very long time, and there is no reason why the macabre diffusionist arguments that the Indians have lived with so long should not be thoroughly exposed for what they are worth.

I find Thapar's emphasis on 'freedom of expression' very intriguing. The historical group of which Thapar is an eminent member came into being in the early 1970s "to give a national direction to an objective and scientific writing of history and to have rational presentation and interpretation of history", as the website of the Indian Council of Historical Research declared. To argue that there was no 'objective and scientific writing of history' till this group moved into government-sponsored power to control the funding and job-opportunities of historical research in India was distinctly reminiscent of a dictatorial streak in itself. By then historical research in the country had flourished for more than a century and to argue that the previous historians were unaware of 'objective and scientific writing of history' was a vicious piece of self-aggrandisement on the part of this group. In fact, since the coming of this group to power, the world of Indian historical studies has been largely criminalised. When Thapar preaches in favour of historical tolerance, one cannot but help feel amused.

I find it very curious that for all her pontifications in the field of ancient India, Thapar forgets to mention that the study of ancient Indian history and archaeology is only a marginal subject in the frame of Indian historical studies. It is difficult to be certain of the precise number, but certainly less than twenty university departments offer full courses in the subject. Archaeology is professionally taught in places whose total number does not reach even the double-digit. The large Historical Centre which Jawaharlal Nehru University of Delhi has been running for long and of which Thapar is a member does not have any professional archaeology component. Thapar does not even bother to enquire why the study of ancient India remains still marginalised in the Indian university frame and why the historical departments of the Indian universities and colleges are dominantly concerned with 'modern' or British India.

Thapar is inexplicably silent about the need to focus on the socio-politics of the Indian past. Thapar and her associates never forget to turn to whatever Western theories are available in a particular area, but as far as the socio-politics of the Indian historical studies is concerned, they seem to be completely indifferent to it except for shouting against the probable or improbable signs of Hindu fundamentalism. In fact, as I have argued in my *Fifty Years of Indian Archaeology (1960–2010): Journey of a Foot Soldier*, by making too much of fundamentalism, Thapar and her fellow travellers have made fundamentalism almost respectable. The fact that they are silent about the fundamentalism of other non-Hindu religious groups throws clear light on what is their attitude to the Indian religious scene. This attitude is also evident in the following formulation of hers: "If the Census of 1882 had included a column for those who observed a cross-over kind of religion, a mix of Hinduism, Islam and other formal religions, this column would undoubtedly have had the largest number". Was there ever a "cross-over kind of religion, a mix of Hinduism, Islam and other formal religions"? Would believers in Hinduism, Islam and Christianity ever admit this? Thapar's tacit assumption is that Hinduism would not have been shown as the religion of the Indian majority, if only the columns of the 1882 census were framed differently.

If one has to appreciate her reference to "a cross-over kind of religion", one must realize that academic interest in them is fairly early, going back to H.H. Wilson's *Sketch of the Religious Sects of the Hindus* in 1846 and Akshay Kumar Datta's *Bharatiya Upasdak Sampraday* in Bengali (Vol. 1 in 1871, Vol. 2 in 1882). *Kartabhaja Sampradaya* (literally, the community which follows the master's or Karta's precepts)which came into existence in the 17th century and continues in some form till today in the Nadia district of West Bengal is a better known example of such communities along with the *Bauls*, *Sahebdhanis,* and others in Bengal. They emerged in different places and times, and although at the grass-roots level they display independent features like the emphasis on *Prema* or love both as a concept and a ritual practice among the *Kartabhajas*, they were by and large tied to the main religious streams of the day. The *Kartabhajas*, for instance, had disciples from the Muslim community but basically they belonged to the Hindu tradition and laid emphasis on different streams of Hindu thought including Gaudiya Vaishavism. The situation in Bengal is understood at least on a general level by most Bengali scholars, but it may be important to have an idea, however brief, of the situation outside Bengal.

The implications of the existence of such communities, apparently on a wide pan-Indian level, while studying the religious universe of India have been recently discussed by Nayanjot Lahiri, and I quote extensively from an unpublished paper on the theme by her ("Archaeology, shrine guardians and the Buddhist revival in colonial India through the microsm of Sanchi", paper presented at 'Conference on Buddhist Revival in Asia' in Singapur, December 15-16, 2011).

> A marked feature of modern India (and no doubt, of earlier periods as well...) has been the presence of heterogeneities within the major religious traditions which militate against present-day ideas of pure or universal religious communities as the categories of Hindu, Muslim, Buddhist and Sikh would tend to suggest. This is was well summed up by Shail Mayaram who, in her description of the "complex ethnic universe"

of South Asia, pointed to the phenomena of communities which had dual or triple religious affiliations, a phenomenon which also figured in many a census report where there are Hindus who appear to be animists, Buddhists who are also shamanistic, and 'Muhammadans' who are Hindus. It is for the same reason that Harjot Oberoi is known to have commented that "it is all very well for historians of religion to think, speak and write about Islam, Hinduism and Sikhism, but they rarely pause to consider if such clear-cut categories actually found expression in the consciousness, actions and cultural performances of the human actors they describe.

What is striking, however, is that while many South Asian religions were marked by an untidy blend of diverse practices, from the nineteenth century onwards, one can also observe a marked consolidation of groups that strongly and self-consciously attempted to 'return' to a more monolithic or what they considered to be the original 'true' forms of those traditions.

So, for instance, in the case of Hinduism, the much cited description offered by Alfred Lyall in 1884, based on his observations and experience in the Indian province of Berar—where the worship of "mere stocks and stones and of local configurations, which are unusual or grotesque in size, shape or position" coexisted quite happily with the "supreme gods of Hinduism, and of their ancient incarnations and personifications, handed down by the Brahmanic scriptures"—highlights the religion's diverse strands. Around the same time that Lyall was writing, these appear to be the very diversities that were sought to be ironed out by the Arya Samaj. Founded in 1875 by Swami Dayanand Saraswati, the

Arya Samaj version of Hinduism, with an emphasis on the infallibility of the Vedas, rejected idol worship, worship of multiple gods and goddesses as also all Hindu avataras.

Similarly, among Muslims in South Asia, there appear to have been multiple strands of thought and practice. There was, on the one hand, a reinvigoration of the Chishti Sufis and the Shi'a effloresences in Awadh and Bengal, along with the visibility of Muslim communities whose 'Hindu' practices are well documented such as the Meos who composed the Mewati *Mahabharata* in the early eighteenth century and the Muslims of the Santhal Parganas who were known to carry sacred water to the shrine of Baidyanath. On the other hand, the nineteenth century was marked by Islamic reform and revival movements that positioned themselves as movements that sought to return to 'true' Islam. This was, as Barbara Metcalf noted, evident in the eschewing of customary practices and in the tendency "to be 'scripturalist' in returning to the written records of the Qur'an and the traditions of the Prophet." In many instances, such movements targeted saints and apostles, especially the *pirs* of Sufi shrines as also practices like pilgrimages and prostration before them.

In the case of Sikhism too, Harjot Oberoi's work has shown that Sikhs could belong to many different traditions. He mentioned the following: Udasi, Nirmala, Khalsa, Nanak-panthi, Ram Raia, Baba Gurditta, Baba Jawahir Singh, Guru Bhag Singh, Nihang, Kalu Panthi, Ram Dasi, Nirankari, Kuka and Sarvaria. As he pointed out, "many of these Sikhs shaved their heads, some smoked tobacco, others were not particular about maintaining the five external symbols of the faith." It was from late nineteenth century onwards, however, that Sikhs in growing numbers took part in campaigns to 'purge' their religion of this diversity and what were viewed as Hindu accretions. By the beginning of the twentieth century, this new identity came to be known as 'Tat Khalsa.'

The nineteenth century revival of Buddhism shared many of these elements. For one, it was marked by attempts to bring Buddhism into conformity with its early doctrines, and this redefinition encompassed various parts of Asia, from Ceylon to Burma and Siam. In Burma, for instance, the Buddhist religion of the bulk of the province was described in the 1891 Census Report as "a thin veneer of philosophy laid over the main structure of Shamanistic belief" to which the 1901 Census Report added that Buddhism was the "superficial polish" while animism "supply the solid constituents that hold the faith together." During the reign of King Mindon (1852–78), however, royal Buddhism became the patron and promoter of Pali orthodoxy. In Ceylon as well, there were various Buddhist fraternities that prescribed adherence to the religion's early principles and doctrines. In the case of Ceylon, the protestant nature of reforms owed a great deal to the challenge that Christian missions posed. Kitsiri Malalgoda has demonstrated that the Buddhist response to Christianity assumed a coherent form only in the latter half of the nineteenth century and that the outcome of the confrontation was the emulation of the model of Protestant Christianity by Buddhists:

.... The number of Buddhists in India were few but not as few as is generally believed. In the 1901 census, for example, the Buddhists in Bengal were said to be 237,893 while there were 35,000 in Kashmir, roughly

> 7000 in Spiti, Lahaul and Kanawar (which then formed part of Panjab), some 9000 in Assam and a small colony of 1000 Buddhists called Saraks in the Tributary States of Orissa. In terms of numbers, they were far more numerous than Hindu reformist groups like the Arya Samaj (whose adherents were about 92,419) and the Brahmo Samaj (with 4050 adherents), even if they did not enjoy the same visibility. The varieties of Buddhism that were practised by most of these communities, in fact, have not been closely studied but whatever is available in the official publications of British India, suggests that these were not closely related to the ancient canon. An instance in point is that of the Orissa Saraks—a name which is said to be derived from Sravaka ('a hearer')—who worshipped Chaturbhuja. Usually, Chaturbhuja is applied to Vishnu but was said to be identified by the Saraks with the Buddha. There were also heterogeneous social practices in the monastic community within one region as, for example, in Spiti (then in Panjab and now in Himachal Pradesh) where, at one end of the spectrum was the celibate Gelukpa sect to which the principal and richest monastery at Ki belonged and at the other end was the Dukhpa sect which permitted its monks to marry.

The importance of this analysis by Lahiri lies in the fact that it makes us sharply aware of the fluid lines of the major and minor organisms which constitute and no doubt have constituted the South Asian religious universe. This also strongly drives home the point that historical analysis based on the assumption of monolithic religious categories in South Asia is likely to be lopsided, if not downright wrong.

While it is obvious that Indian religious groups, if studied figuratively under a microscope, will reveal many shades of groupings and beliefs across religious boundaries, it would be equally and grievously wrong historically to imagine that the major groups like Hinduism, Buddhism, etc. were only artificial groupings. Nobody is clamouring for the establishment of a 'pure and unblemished' Hindu identity but that is no reason why the very existence of Hinduism as a religious entity in Indian history should be doubted. For a long time some Indologists have been trying to argue that if only the nineteenth century census operators had tabulated the Indian Hindu population according to their individual obligations to the tenets of Vaishnavism, Saivism, etc. Hinduism would not have emerged as the majority religion of the country. This attitude clearly displays unhappiness on the part of these scholars to give the status of majority religion in India to Hinduism. Thapar apparently belongs to this group because otherwise she would not have raised the issue of the nineteenth century census operators: Hinduism is considered the majority religion of India because the first census operators followed a wrong methodology of religious enumeration. I would call it a kind of 'Hindu-baiting', based on the mistaken belief that in Hinduism the two levels, the lowermost level of animism, etc. and the highest level of Upanishadic monotheism with other levels of sacredness in between, are irreconciliable and that the same may be said about the sectarian differences between Siva, Vishnu and others. In contrast, a devout Hindu like me has no difficulty at all in making obeisance to a large flowering *Palash* (*Butea frondosa*) tree and following it up, if called upon to do so, by worshipping at the shrine of any of the three members of the Hindu trinity in the course of the day. In my mind and—I am sure—in the minds of innumerable fellow Hindus, there is absolutely no contradiction in this type of Hindu religious behaviour. It would be historically a case of bad judgement if Hinduism is conceived only as a disjointed scatter of multiple sacred beliefs and sects. In fact, this is a non-issue, when it comes to judging the significance of Hinduism in ancient India. The way Hinduism has functioned (or still functions) at the grass-roots level throughout history is no doubt a valid academic point of enquiry but that is no reason why the frame of Hinduism as a belief system should be abandoned as a historical category.

Thapar refers to the formation of different identities in modern India but does not mention that it is important to understand the historical assumptions behind the formations of such identities. For instance, if there is a *Dalit* version of the history of ancient India, we must understand what it is and what is the presence or absence of historical logic behind it. The formation of historical identities cannot be avoided, and it is only by discussing its basis threadbare that one can focus on its true worth or rather, the lack of it. In the case of India, Thapar, in an interview to the French paper *Le Monde*, foresaw (cited by M. Danino in *Dialogue*, April-June 2006/vol. 7, no.4) that by the end of the 21st century India would break down into a series of small states federated within a more viable single economic space on the scale of the subcontinent. For those of us who refuse to play the role of a clairvoyant as far as our national fate is concerned and are deeply pained by the thought of further national disintegration, we must try to understand the historical basis of 'identities'. The study of the socio-politics of the ancient Indian past should play an increasing role in the understanding of the ways in which ancient Indian history has been interpreted and how they are linked to the formation of identities in modern India.

The tragedy of ancient historical research in modern India is that without trying to force open new grounds of empirical research it got involved primarily in the political feuds of the historians and different kinds of mostly indefensible theoretical structures.

Bhakti, i.e. Adoration for Western Ancient Indian and Archaeological Scholarship in Post-Independence India.

Those of us, who believe that the Western universities are full of people with wholly scholarly and rational attitudes to the ancient past, may read with profit what Professor C.C. Lamberg-Karlovsky has written about the attitude of a colleague of his at Harvard. We are deeply thankful to Dr. S. Kalyanaraman (*bharatkalyan97.blogspot.com*) for drawing our attention to this. Many years ago a former student of mine faced almost an identical situation in the Oriental Faculty of Cambridge (UK). He was made to stumble in his pre-Ph.D. registration test because he did not cite, or did not do extensive justice to the theory that the death of the Buddha was about hundred years later than the generally accepted date of *c.* 486 BC or thereabouts.

I quote from Dr. Kalyanaraman:

> As I read through Bryan K. Wells, 2011, *Epigraphic Approaches to Indus Writing*, Oxford and Oakville, Oxbow Books, some disturbing points emerge, related to academic prejudices in adjudicating a student's contributions.
>
> In the Foreword to the book, C.C. Lamberg-Karlovsky, makes some incisive observations and comments on how Bryan's doctoral dissertation was dealt with in the academic setting of Harvard University: "Bryan Wells... came to Harvard as a graduate student intent on continuing his study of the Indus Civilization and its

script... He was, and remains, committed to the idea that the Indus script represents writing and its decipherment will lead to an understanding of its texts and language. He did not think that at Harvard his dedication to this goal would meet with resistance. It did. This volume is a substantially revised edition of his doctoral dissertation. Bryan's dissertation committee consisted of myself as Chair and Dr. Richard Meadow and Professor Michael Witzel. A near final draft of his dissertation was rejected by Meadow and Witzel. Bryan was required to return from Germany to confront and ostensibly to correct and address its shortcomings. The basic problem was that Professor Witzel, influenced by Steve Farmer, had concluded that the Indus script was neither writing nor representative of language. (See 'The Collapse of the Indus Script Thesis: The Myth of Literate Harappan Civilization' by Steve Farmer, Richard Sproat and Michael Witzel, 2004, http://www.safarmer.com/downloads).

Steve Farmer believes the Indus signs to be magical symbols. In light of Professor Witzel's strong commitment to the non-writing nature of the Indus script Bryan's effort was deemed spurious and unacceptable. Richard Meadow, less strident in his view as to the nature of the Indus script, nevertheless advised Bryan to 'tone down' his view that the Indus represented 'writing'. Approximately six weeks were spent as Professor Witzel balked at any mention of the Indus being a script and having a logo-syllabic nature. He insisted that Bryan substatute the word 'marks' or 'symbols' for script. He was initially in opposition to the entire thesis. A Professor's opinion, which, in this case is a minority view within the profession, should never be used to impose or prevent an alternative hypothesis from

> being addressed by a Ph.D. candidate. It was not as if Bryan was addressing an untenable, absurd hypothesis. He was to spend weeks of uncertainty, anxiety, and, in a state of near depression he puzzled over what to do. The consternation endured and expenses incurred effects his entire family. " (pp. xiii-xv)

Eventually good sense prevailed, and the student got his Ph.D. In the case of the Cambridge Oriental Faculty student I mentioned (an Indian), he slowly realized the importance of not being on the wrong side of the supervisor's and his friends' opinion and was eventually successful in getting his degree.

In the wake of the Farmer-Sproat-Witzel theory, some Indian computer scientists had pursued some methodologies specific to computational techniques and reached the conclusion that the system of Indus signs was likely to represent a regular writing system. Even without knowing anything about computational techniques, one may do some serious advocacy in favour of the idea that the Indus Civilization was indeed familiar with writing. First, very few of the available signs were regularly used, suggesting that the total corpus of the texts was likely to be much larger than the corpus which is currently available. In view of the long-standing Indian tradition of writing on perishable materials such as birch and palm-leaves, this hypothesis is certainly worthy of consideration. Further, a famous Indian archaeologist, B.B. Lal (*How Deep are the Roots of Indian Civilization? Archaeology Answers.* Delhi 2009) has drawn attention to a terracotta representation of a tablet among the excavated antiquities of Mohenjo-daro. The point is that identically shaped wooden writing tablets are still widely used in the village schools of northern India. The very existence of the terracotta representation of such a tablet among the excavated antiquities of Mohenjo-daro goes a long way to suggest that a regular schooling system where children would use wooden writing tablets on which they would practice their art of writing was in place in this civilization, which is hardly a matter of surprise in view of the fact that both in Egypt and Mesopotamia, schools were known.

The fact that some Western scholars of Harvard seem to have closed their mind to the possibility of the Indus Civilization having a writing system, much of which has not survived, may be seen as a part of a generally prevalent current Western attitude regarding the originality and antiquity of the Indian civilization.

Even if we set the last point aside, the implication of the possibility that there was a regular schooling system in the Indus Civilization is enormous. First, this will mean that the general Indian system of writing on perishable materials was then very much in place and that the extent and level of this civilization's literacy was much wider than what has hitherto been thought. *Secondly, in the light of this possibility we have to revise our prevalent opinion that literacy died with the end of the Indus Civilization. If there was a regular system of imparting literacy and learning through schools, the literary tradition is most unlikely to have completely withered away. More importantly, this also raises doubts about the possibility that India had ever passed through a phase marked by the absence of writing.* The whole argument is no doubt circumstantial but the shapes of the Mohenjo-daro terracotta specimens and the wooden tablets widely used in some village schools till recently are absolutely identical. In fact, their similarity is as close as the similarity between the terracotta representation of a *Siva-linga* found in the Harappan context at Kalibangan and the modern examples of *Siva-lingas*.

The point is that our argument can straightaway be denied but at the same time this raises points about which our attitude should be open. Among other things, *this has the effect of making the Indus Civilization stand at the apex of a continuous Indian literary tradition.*

Regarding the date of the *Mahaparinirvana* of the Buddha, the issue we raised earlier in this section, one may point out that the issue has been extensively debated since the late nineteenth century and there was no point in waking up in the 1980s to the possibility that it could be a hundred years later than its commonly accepted date. It is an old debate, and the only advantage for some Western scholars in propagating this late date was that it would root out the possibility of any Buddhist philosophical impact on any aspect of ancient Greek thought.

The denial of antiquity and originality to the ancient Indian civilization is not limited only to the Western (read 'white') scholars. It is quite clear in the writings of many Indian professionals. In fact, the list is so long that it would be futile to list them in detail. *Bhakti*, i.e. adoration for Western ancient Indian and archaeological scholarship, is still enormous.

On the Western side, *Bhakti* for the Western ancient Indian and archaeological scholarship is kept alive by offering inducements of various kinds. For instance, the European Association of South Asian Archaeologists brings over, with full cost, 10 or more Indian scholars to their biennial conferences of archaeologists, historians and art historians. As I have recently explained the situation in my article in *Oxford Handbook of Public Archaeology* (2012), the proceedings of these conferences are published in

> volumes which do not usually reach Indian bookshops or libraries. However, they unfailingly set apart a sum of money for bringing in important Indian participants—about ten to twelve of them. To the Indian invitees this counts as a badge of honour, so to speak. None of these

> important Indian archaeologists can, of course, even dream of being critical of the ideas which emanate from the pens of the learned European archaeologists interested in South Asia just as none of these learned Euro-American archaeologists can pass up a chance of feeling superior to the native Indian archaeologists. It is a funny world in which the Indian archaeologists hankering after so-called international recognition accept their minor role without demur and are unfailing in their praise of the work done by their Euro-American colleagues.

An unusual expression of *Bhakti* of this kind has been noticed in the Government of India celebration of the 150 years of the Archaeological Survey of India in December 2011 when a Cambridge emeritus professor of archaeology, Lord Colin Renfrew, was invited to give what were described as two 'curtain-raising' lectures before the celebrations were formally inaugurated by the Prime Minister. It is important to note that Lord Renfrew, who, incidentally, is not known to have taken any specific interest in Indian archaeology, was not invited to lecture at an Indian academic institution, which would have been appropriate, but he was given the task of virtually introducing archaeology as a theme to the formal start of the official celebrations of the Government of India. In the same vein, a British freelance historian was invited to write a book, at the Government of India expense (at the expense of the National Cultural Fund, if one learns correctly), on the history of Indian archaeology to coincide with the celebrations. It is indeed unthinkable that Indian archaeologists will ever be invited to be involved in the celebratory ceremonies of a British national institution ! There cannot be any doubt that the present leadership of the Archaeological Survey of India and its officially superior organization, the Ministry of Culture, had completely ignored the fact that the Survey was a national organization of an independent country and that the celebration of its 150 years did not call for any 'inauguratory' role by foreign archaeologists.

The dimensions of this *Bhakti* network run deeper. As I explicitly pointed out in my article in *Oxford Handbook of Public Archaeology*,

> The relationship with First World archaeologists with field interests in the Third World can also be a political issue in Third World archaeology. In Indian archaeology, for instance, it assumes an identifiable dimension. In view of the fact that the government of India seems to be currently in favour of an open-arms policy regarding the participation of foreign archaeologists in Indian archaeology, the situation is likely to deteriorate further in the future. The signs we already have are ominous. It is known that in the early days of European control of India, there used to be a class of Indian merchants who were known as the *Banyans* or *Dubashes.* Their approach to business success was to act as brokers of a European business house or a European merchant. It is these Indian merchants who paved the way for the European economic and political domination of India. In Indian archaeology, there are already a number of university centres whose ostensible academic mission is to provide collaboration to foreign archaeologists in return for authorships in publications and sundry incentives like 'visiting fellowships' and all-expenses-paid trips to international conferences. This also absolves them of the duty of doing research on their own. This 'Banyan or Dubash model' of doing archaeology is the prevailing rage among Indian university archaeologists.

This tide of *Bhakti* is also reinforced by a rapidly developing situation in the area of Indian historical education. Now that Sanskrit has ceased to be a compulsory subject in Indian school education, the students' understanding of their own regional languages has begun to grow weak. In my classes in Delhi University History department till the late 1980s, I noticed a distinct division between the students who were educated till then in the vernacular medium of instruction and those who were educated in the medium of English. The students of the latter class were hardly familiar with their rich vernacular literary traditions depicting the different nuances of the land. They were, in fact, somewhat aggressive to assert their imagined 'Western identity'. The teachers themselves belonged mostly to this group, and the first thing required was whether these students were familiar with the Western historical and archaeological approaches to ancient India. It was not a happy development even in the late 1980s, and in the current context the situation has possibly become far more aggravated. Any kind of commitment to the ancient past of the nation, of which they are the lineal descendants and of which there should be at least a modicum of pride in their minds, is generally missing in the historical writings of this generation of young people, whether students or teachers. Now that there is a manifest concern with the real ideological threats of 'breaking India' (R. Malhotra and A. Neelakandan, *Breaking India, Western Intervention in Dravidian and Dalit Faultlines*, Delhi 2011), our ideas regarding our ancient history may be more important than we know or care for. In other words, it is getting more imperative to view ancient India in its own terms than the lenses of those who would rather view it as a past with which they would not have any emotional link. The American archaeologists approach the ancient Indian past in the same way they approach the past of the American Iraquois tribe which is something completely unrelated to them. There are indications that in a large section of Indian archaeologists and ancient historians this American approach is an eminently acceptable approach. The signs of 'intellectualism' in this section of Indian writings on ancient India are almost exclusively the authors' familiarity with the related writings of Western scholars. This is how they thrive in the academia linked to the Indian ancient history scenario from Romila Thapar to Upinder Singh.

The history of Indology in Germany and elsewhere has been a matter of academic attention in the recent years, three convenient examples of which are *Aryans, Jews, Brahmins, Theorizing Authority through Myths of Identity* by D. Figueira (2002), *Indology, Indomania, Orientalism: Ancient India's Rebirth in Modern Germany* by D. McGetchin (2009), and Indra Sengupta, *From Salon to Discipline: State, University and Indology in Germany 1821-1914* (2005). Although all these works of research contain many new data and perspectives, none of them prefers to dwell particularly on the basic racist milieu of the growth of Indological studies in Euro-America. From roughly the mid-nineteenth century onward that milieu has been dominated entirely by racist attitudes to the subject of these Euro-American studies, i.e. India and Indians. It is not that this racism matters to a large section of Indians. *Bhakti* for Western scholarship in ancient Indian history and archaeology runs too deep in the Indian mind. One learns that somebody as racist as Max Müller in his evaluation of the potential of India and Indians has had a stamp issued in his honour by the Indian Post and Telegraphs in 1974. One may also take note of the title of an Indian publication, *Indology and Its Eminent Western Savants: Collection of Biographies of Western Indologists* by G.G. Sengupta (1996). *The Max Müller type of racism where a very superior attitude in relation to modern*

India and Indians is commonplace, still persists unabashedly in the various Indian studies sections of many Euro-American universities.

Equally bypassed in such studies in the history of Western Indology is the issue of the ecclesiastical pressure to translate ancient texts in the hope that conversion to Christianity would be easier once the message of the true state of Hinduism and its changing characters were driven home to the public. That was the main reason why Lieutenant Colonel Joseph Boden instituted a Sanskrit professorship (Boden professorship) in Oxford in 1832. Joseph Boden was an East India Company official from Kolkata, and he donated £25000 to Oxford. He is said to have held the opinion that "a more general and critical knowledge of the Sanskrit language will be a means of enabling his countrymen to proceed in the conversion of the natives of India to the Christian religion, by disseminating a knowledge of the sacred scriptures amongst them, more effectually than all other means whatsoever" (*The Oxford University Calender* of 1832, p. 50).

The institution of the Sanskrit professorship in Cambridge in 1867 is not at all dissimilar, though, in this case the university itself seems to have taken the initiative. The first holder of the post, E.B. Cowell, had among his referees Bishop Cotton of Kolkata. From the Bishop's point of view, as he stated in a letter dated 11 July 1867, the main claim of Cowell to the post lay in the fact that, as befitted somebody aspiring to "a professorship in a Christian university", he was not a person whose interest in India was confined to philology and ancient learning *but that he was also "actively desirous to see it a Christian country" and that his influence in any position "would be exerted with a distinct reference to that great end"* (italics added). In his inaugural lecture in 1867, Cowell hoped that India might under British rule "share the blessings of Western civilization and Christianity."

To facilitate India's conversion to Christianity was also the aim of F. Max Müller's translation of *The Hymns of the Rigveda, with Sayana's Commentary* (London, 1849-75, 6 volumes), which was largely supported by the East India Company's Board of Directors. He wrote in the following terms to his wife:

> The translation of the Veda will hereafter tell to a great extent on the fate of India and on the growth of millions of souls in that country. It is the root of their religion, and to show them what the root is, I feel sure, is the only way of uprooting all that has sprung from it during the last 3000 years.

The official sanction to open India to the proselytisation of Christianity came about in the Charter Act of the British Parliament in 1813. The missionaries, as Figueira puts it,

> They thought Indians were suffering in darkness and languishing in horrid conditions. One of these leading evangelists was Charles Grant, who returned from India in 1794 and sat on the Board of Directors. Grant modelled his evangelical mission for Britain on the Roman empire, with the idea that they were spreading civilization. Grant portrayed Hinduism as rotten to its core, incapable of restoration or renaissance.

According to another contemporary evangelist, "the Hindu divinities were absolutely monsters of lust, injustice, wickedness and cruelty. In short their religious system is one grand abomination."

Even missionaries like William Carey, who are known for their contributions to the modernisation of vernacular presses, had always their eyes focussed on the importance of such establishments in the propagation of Christianity. That was also the attitude of Cowell who emphasized the close links between Sanskrit and the vernacular literatures and thought that through an improvement of the latter one could look forward to an improvement in the situation of the Hindus.

The study of Sanskrit got linked not merely to the programme of evangelical Christianity but also to specific race issues in the form of Aryanism. The political ramifications of this issue can be clearly perceived in the generally prevalent assumption that the Aryans were the first Western conquerors of India. Macdonell in his book on the history of Sanskrit literature states this explicitly. This assumption was firmly in place by the beginning of the 20th century.

Even in the initiation and patronage of Indian archaeology, it was not wholly because of an altruistic belief. There was a notion in the background that archaeological enquiries would show that Hinduism was not always the most powerful religion in India by yielding many remains of Buddhism. The basic attitude still persists. Scholars are criticised for stating that the ancient Indian civilization was a Hindu civilization. It is conveniently forgotten that Buddhism sprang out of Hinduism as a basically reform movement against the all-pervasive importance given to the performance of Vedic rituals. In this sense, Hinduism has been the tree trunk from which various religious offshoots like Buddhism have emerged throughout history. If the offshoots became subsequently powerful on their own, that need not detract from the significance of the original trunk.

It was after Independence that *Bhakti* towards Western archaeological theories began to grow distinctly visible. Uncritical acceptance of Western opinions in archaeological matters had been by and large the order of the day. The importance which the Indian scholars attached to every little opinion of Mortimer Wheeler whose introduction to Indian archaeology took place during his brief stay in the country as the Director General of the Archaeological Survey of India (1944–48) is fairly distressing, but the tragedy is that this attitude still continues. In two or more western Indian university archaeological departments that I can think of (Deccan College, Pune and MS University, Baroda), it is almost obligatory for teachers and students to begin the writing of anything on the Indus Civilization by quoting what some American Indus specialists think of it. In the case of the Indus studies, the position once enjoyed by Wheeler seems to have gone to J.M. Kenoyer, an American archaeologist of Madison, Wisconsin. A paper of mine on the archaeology of Indian religions, which was commissioned by the Oxford Centre of Hindu Studies or something like that, was rejected for publication by the same Centre because, this paper, according to one of its referees (an Indian lady of JNU who was associated with this centre under a fellowship programme named after an Indian family), did not take into consideration Kenoyer's opinion. If Kenoyer has published anything significant on the religion of the Indus Civilization, I am not aware of it, but to this Indian university teacher, that was no reason why Kenoyer should not be cited in an article on the religious aspects of the Indus civilization. The unusual grip of this American gentleman on Indian archaeology will also be clear from the fact that he was asked to give the Presidential lecture to the Indian Archaeological Society in its session in Lucknow in the winter of 2011, and apparently in return for this privilege, he arranged in 2012 an archaeological study/conference tour of Pakistan for a number of Indian archaeologists from Vadodara and Pune (and elsewhere) who are known to be obliged to him in various ways. This group of Indian archaeologists included the Secretary of the Indian Archaeological Society. I believe that the Indian Archaeological Society is still indebted in various ways to people sympathetic to the RSS, but retaining the independence of Indian archaeological research is in no way their concern. In such matters there is hardly any difference between the RSS and the Indian left. One has, after all, to look after one's personal interests!

While talking about the *Bhakti* of the Indian archaeologists towards their foreign *gurus*, one must draw attention to the book written by a former Director of the National Museum and a former senior officer of the Archaeological Survey of India, Dr. N.R. Banerjee, on the beginning of iron in India. The book was his Ph.D. thesis supervised by N.R. Ray of Calcutta University. Much of Banerjee's book *The Iron Age in India* (1965) is concerned with what he thought was the Aryan problem, and all that he basically did was to quote learned Western scholars on this topic, without even pausing to consider whether that made any sense. On the other hand, a somewhat later review of the existing data on Indian iron (*Antiquity* 1976) showed that the basic facts regarding Indian iron suggested, in no uncertain terms, that India was an independent and early centre of iron metallurgy. The tragedy is that this simple fact was realized by scholars including European metallurgists till basically the 1930s but was forgotten by Indian archaeologists in the post-Independence phase.

I believe that I have pointed out unequivocally that nation has hardly blipped in the intellectual radar of our ancient historians and archaeologists of the post-Independence period. In the pre-Independence period there were at least some questionings at the periphery of the basic colonial assumptions, but after Independence, we decided to remain uncritical and mindful of only our personal gains.

Notes: (1) *Excavations at Rakhigarhi* (2013 >) After the volume was sent to the press, the following development has taken place in Indian archaeology. Vasant Shinde of the Deccan College, a long-time collaborator of Japanese and American archaeologists, has been granted permission by the Archaeological Survey of India under the Director Generalship of Gautam Sengupta to conduct excavations at Rakhigarhi in Haryana, which would be funded by the Global Heritage Fund. It is worth putting on record that this is the first time that a foreign NGO has been allowed to bear the expenses of an excavation in India. It must be noted that there is no lack of funds for conducting excavations in India. I have repeatedly heard young friends in the Archaeological Survey of India and the universities proclaiming that money is not a problem to do fieldwork. So, the first question one has to ask is if the Deccan College which is funded 100% by the Maharashtra government sought funds from the government and/or University Grants Commission and other (cf. Indian Council of Historical Research) sources for its Rakhigarhi excavations. My assumption is that funds have been sought from a foreign NGO with some specific purpose in mind. Secondly, as NGOs of this kind are not really charitable organizations and generally act as the front of a large number of people in the background, we can expect various kinds of foreign 'Indus experts' trying to take over the 'Indus' scene and lecturing us Indians how to do Indus archaeology. Secondly, this is the first time that such a large and important site in India has been handed over to foreign funding and thus foreign control. Thirdly, the way permission has been granted to re-excavate the site when the report on the first spell of work there is under preparation is ethically unacceptable. Apparently, the powers behind the issue of this permission are not concerned with archaeological ethics or the national interest of the country in the domain of archaeology. I would like to emphasize that from these points of view, the Global Heritage Fund participation in the Rakhigarhi excavations under Vasant Shinde of the Deccan College marks a watershed in the history of Indian archaeology. From now on, there will be increasingly successful attempts to take over Indian archaeology from the Indians by miscellaneous groups of racially arrogant people masquerading as archaeologists under the umbrella of various foreign NGOs.

(2) Another instance of Indian *bhakti* in Western scholarship has been expressed recently by the Director of the Kerala Council of Historical Research, P.J. Cherian in *The Hindu* (25 December 2013). According to this report, a memorandum of understanding was signed between the Indian Council of Historical Research (funded 100% by the Government of India) and a six-member Oxford tem led by Nicole Boivin of the School of Archaeology in Oxford in April 2010. Whether Nicole Boivin could sign such a document on behalf of her university and whether the ICHR could formally accept such a document signed by her are important matters, but here we do not have to go into that question. What matters is Cherian's statement:

> This is for the first time in the history of post-Independent India that Oxford University is collaborating with an Indian institution on such a research project.

Apparently Cherian takes this as a badge of honour and this is his way of answering his critics at the Indian Archaeological Society meeting in Thiruvanthapuram in 2011 when M.G.S. Narayanan, a former chairmen of the ICHR, wanted the Pattinam project to be handed over to the Archaeological Survey of India. That he should try to do so by invoking blessings from Oxford is typical of the patheic *bhakti* displayed by some Indians for Western scholarship. Incidentally, the Oxford characters mentioned in this connection, C. Gosden and W. Morrison, have never been interested in Indian archaeology and their presence in this project is irrelevant from the Indian point of view. The Pattinam excavations under Cherian have also began to attract some Biblical and Jewish scholarly interest, making the whole thing look like an unholy conglomeration of various interest groups. It is time the Government of India took serious notice of these groups.

2

Comptroller and Auditor General's Report on Indian Museum, Victoria Memorial, Asiatic Society, National Library and Kala Bhavan, Visva Bharati

How Cultural Institutions Function in Modern India?

The CAG reports are a familiar feature of the Indian governmental scene. They are submitted to Parliament, and although they are supposed to be in the public domain after that, not much interest is taken in them unless they come to the attention of the media. Various CAG reports have made history in recent years, but the reports mentioned in the present paper do not fall in that category. The report on the first three institutions here is dated 2005 {Report No 4 of 2005 (civil)}. The report on Visva Bharati is dated 2007 (Report No 3 of 2007) and that on National Library is dated 2010-11 (Report No 3 of 2010-11). All these institutions possess innumerable varieties of culturally precious items including paintings by famous modern Indian painters which are kept in Kala Bhavan and

Ravindra Bhavan of Visva Bharati. National Library and Victoria Memorial possess collections which are both rare and precious, and as the repositories of the ancient materials, the significance of Indian Museum and Asiatic Society can hardly be overstated. The way these important institutions, funded almost exclusively by the central government, operate may be an eye-opener on how the institutions dealing with 'culture' function in modern India. Not many of us know anything about the inner functioning of these and other organizations of this kind. We may be suitably impressed by the cultural landmarks of Kolkata in the form of the grand façades of Indian Museum and National Library and take pride in the historic significance of both Asiatic Society and Visva Bharati, but as the CAG reports testify, they have been violating every principle of the business for which they are supposed to exist. The only bright thing in the whole dismal affair is the quality of the CAG reports themselves. Precise and with clearly defined objectives, they cut through the rigmarole surrounding these institutions and are a credit to the team of the bright young professionals of the relevant branch of the CAG establishment.

INDIAN MUSEUM, VICTORIA MEMORIAL HALL AND ASIATIC SOCIETY

These three institutions, established respectively in 1814, 1903 and 1784 respectively, have, among their functions, the acquisition, conservation, preservation and documentation of historically significant objects. Some amount of research in each of these fields is implicitly necessary for the satisfactory performance of each of these functions, but research has been by and large only a sporadic activity of the Indian institutions of this type and depends on the individual initiatives of the people in charge. In the case of Asiatic Society, especially after the declaration of its national importance under the Asiatic Society Act of 1984, in the wake of which a number of research staff were recruited from mainly among the retired university academics, some importance is given to research. The primary step to judge the research credibility of any organization is the consistency of the publication record of its members. The CAG teams decided to ignore the research aspect of these organizations from their purview, focussing exclusively on how the objects in their collections have been acquired, preserved, conserved and documented.

Examined in detail, the issue of acquisition suggests that the acquisition of historically significant objects was a low priority of all these three institutions. The total number of purchased objects in Indian Museum in 1999–2004 was 168, with the percentage of total expenditure on the acquisition of artefacts to the museum's total expenditure during this period being only 4.36. These figures for Victoria Memorial for the same period were 319 and 19.09 respectively. Asiatic Society purchased during this period 115 objects, spending 2.24 % of this period's total capital expenditure. There is one more noteworthy feature about the acquisition process. The process itself is shoddy, without any specific policy or target and without an iota of professionalism. Objects are acquired virtually on the basis of the seller's opinion of its antiquity and context.

The CAG report emphasizes that "none of these institutions established standards or benchmarks for the acquisition and valuation of artefacts". It cites the following case as an example.

> In December 2003, the Indian Museum acquired two pieces of African ivory carvings with human figures on two elephant tasks along with one set of chess pieces.

> The decision to purchase these items was taken by the Purchase Committee in November 2003 based merely on a statement made by the individual seller that these artefacts were collected from African countries by her mother-in-law. The antiquity of the artefacts was not established nor was the claim of the seller of Rs. 10 lakh verified. As against the original price demanded by the seller, the price paid by the Museum was Rs. 5.5 lakh. The basis or the consideration on which the final price was arrived at was not on record. Further, there was no evidence to establish that the artefacts deserved a place among the Museum objects.

To anybody familiar with the world of museums, this example and the procedure which was followed in this case are likely to seem bizarre. The responsibility lies not merely with the institutions' administrative establishments but also with their 'purchase committees', the members of which are selected principally from the local academia and bureaucracy. They may or may not have any expertise or enthusiasm for antiquities. In the face of such casually constituted 'purchase committees', the chances of 'fake' antiquities getting into the official registers become naturally very high.

More important is the fact that the lack of any well-defined acquisition policy in these institutions has an effect on the overall fate of historical antiquities in India. It is well known that there is a thriving international market in Indian antiquities, which is illegal in India but perfectly legal in the places where they are openly traded. Visits to the galleries of antiquity dealers at some major international places like London, Zurich and New York will bear out the truth of this statement. A very large percentage of these antiquities has been smuggled out of the country, and as the process has been going on for a very long time and the monetary stakes are very high, one wonders if it can be stopped only by the law enforcement agencies. Another generally ignored dimension of this trade is that the important new finds have begun to show a tendency to be reported first on the websites of international antiquity dealers. I have seen the photographs of large Chandraketugarh terracotta plaques showing village scenes, etc. only on such websites. By being casual about the purchase of historically important antiquities, the three Kolkata institutions of the CAG report are only strengthening the hands of the private antiquity dealers of the city and contributing to that extent to the process of antiquity smuggling. If the antiquity sellers are assured that their collections can be sold for a fair price in the city itself, smuggling is unlikely to be the first choice in this matter. Besides, if these institutions can develop pro-active 'purchase committees' whose members will go out to the countryside to purchase antiquities directly from the villagers, the impact on the local antiquity market may be fairly high. If these procedures are followed by the similar institutions all over India, one may be sure that there will be considerable reduction in the number of antiquities which get smuggled out today.

One has to recall at this point that the present antiquity law of the country expects the villagers or any private individual to declare antiquity finds and produce proper documentation to a government officer at the state level. The person who actually finds the object is not rewarded in any way. This is one of the reasons why people do not report the antiquities they may find in various ways in the countryside. This aspect of the law requires immediate change if we are serious about keeping new finds of antiquities in the country. The museums and other relevant institutions of the area may play a major role in the process.

Again, anybody familiar with the world of Indian museums will know that maintaining up-to-date accession registers of antiquities or publishing their catalogues is not among its strong points. Such registers have to be accompanied by the photographs of each accessioned object which, in this modern world, should also have a digitised record. This is the only way to trace an object if it gets stolen or lost. The CAG team found irregular maintenance of accession registers, inadequate photo-documentation of art objects and similarly inadequate digitisation and computerised documentation process in each of these three institutions. Digitisation has been defined here as "acquiring, converting, storing and providing information in a standardised, organized format and availability on demand from a common system accessible to the users of museum objects for various purposes". The importance of digitisation in any kind of data management in the modern world is obvious. There was no comprehensive and time-bound plan to digitise their collections in any of these three Kolkata institutions. In a sense, they are completely oblivious to the role they are supposed to perform for the better cultural management in the country, although they are nationally funded institutions.

The appalling state of affairs in the accessioning of manuscripts in Asiatic Society has been pointed out by the audit team.

> The Asiatic Society claimed to possess 59,523 art objects as on 31 March 2004 which included 46,994 manuscripts. Out of this, only 28,423 manuscripts (47.74 per cent of total objects) were accessioned till November 2004. Though the majority of objects were yet to be accessioned, the Society never prepared any action plan for completing the work.

The actual task of physical verification of objects seems to be something unknown to these institutions. The audit team's report sounds full of despair:

> None of the three Institutions conducted any physical verification of the art objects possessed by them during the last five years. As such, the physical existence and condition of the art objects as shown in the records of the Institutions could not be ascertained in audit. This fact was repeatedly mentioned in the Separate Audit Reports issued to the Institutes every year.

The litany of woes does not end here. There is a remarkable indifference to the conservation process, with inadequate expenditure being at the top of the list. The conservation laboratory of Indian Museum functioned at the level of 30.94 per cent of its capacity in the five years considered by the CAG team. The state of affairs in this regard in Indian Museum could be clearly understood from a photograph published recently in a Kolkata newspaper, which shows a distinct layer of decayed stone dust around a piece of stone sculpture. Similarly, there is a badly managed security system with ill-trained guards and lack of proper supervision, and one need not be surprised that something as precious as the head of a fifth-century Sarnath Buddha was reported stolen from Indian Museum in December 2004.

What is not easily appreciated is that the conservation laboratories of museums, especially of a major museum like Indian Museum, can be important centres of research on the composition of ancient objects, among other things. British Museum, for instance, has a rich science adjunct including a dating laboratory. There is no reason why the system cannot be emulated in India.

One of the reasons why the museum people go very slow in accessioning objects is that if anything is unaccessioned, they are absolved of any responsibility, if the item goes missing. Many years ago, possibly in the pages of the long-defunct Bengali magazine *Prabasi* (or is it *Bharatavarsha?*) in the 1930s or earlier, there was some discussion on the find of a sculptural panel of pre-Christian era from somewhere in Bhuvaneswar. Sometime in the 1980s I noticed this panel lying in a corner of Ashutosh Museum of Calcutta University along with other miscellaneous finds. Not so long ago I looked for the find in the same place in Ashutosh Museum but found it missing. On enquiry I was told that there was no record of any such thing being acquired by Ashutosh Museum.

In the case of Visva Bharati, one can do no better than cite the 'highlights' of the report.

1. There are several encroachments of the University land. The University failed to take any effective action against encroachers.
2. The University has not made adequate effort to account for and secure the artefacts and other museum objects by applying modern technology like digitization, photo documentation and computerised documentation of the artefacts.
3. No physical verification of movable assets was conducted in the university during last five years except for the museum holdings belonging to Rabindra Bhavana.
4. It was ascertained from the Kala Bhavana that 30 paintings by artists like Rabindranath Tagore, Nandalal Bose and 886 other art objects were missing. No investigation into the matter was conducted.

5. The museums of the University, viz. Rabindra Bhavana and Kala Bhavana are not equipped with modern electronic security gadgets like intruder alarm/CCTV/metal detector, etc.
6. The fire fighting measures in the campus are inadequate. The buildings of the University being old are vulnerable to fire.
7. The expenditure on conservation/restoration showed a decreasing trend during the period under review.
8. In Rabindra Bhavana, 175 artefacts were in damaged condition due to improper preservation. The heritage buildings of Udayana, Punascha, Udichi, Shyamali and Rabindra Bhavana were in dilapidated conditions and needed immediate attention for their restoration and renovation.
9. There was no system in Kala Bhavana to periodically assess the physical condition of artefacts and identify the nature of damages to their art objects.
10. The large number of outdoor sculptures and murals created by famed artists did not find place in any departmental accession register. No Bhavana took any responsibility for the maintenance of some of these priceless outdoor treasures. Many of these objects have already developed signs of degradation due to lack of proper maintenance.

Comments are unnecessary on what has been cited above, but this categorically shows that the theft of the Noble Prize memorabilia from Santiniketan was not an isolated incident but a faithful corollary of the long-standing indifference of the University to the maintenance of proper care and security of the nation's cultural heritage entrusted in its care.

The situation in National Library is no less heart-rending. Priceless possessions in the Rare Books section are exposed to damage and loss, and there is no centralised and computerised catalogue system. Nobody attaches significance to stock verifications. These are only some of the pitfalls which greet an unwary reader in the National Library of the country.

At the end of this long litany of sorrowful lapses in some of the prominent government-funded cultural institutions, we have to ask two questions of ourselves. What is this situation due to? Money, formal government indifference or concerned people on the ground? The situation is due invariably to the 'concerned people on the ground'—the people at the helm of the institutions, the members of the various committees, the staff manning the galleries and different sections of conservation, photography, etc., and above all, an over-arching indifference to, and lack of pride in their role as keepers of a section of the nation's heritage.

The second question is: is this state of affairs characteristic only of these institutions in West Bengal or is it a sign of general malaise of such institutions or organizations all over the country? On the basis of what I have been able to observe in organizations in various parts of the country, I would say that they are also equally subject to the conditions which we have here outlined for a handful of institutions in West Bengal.

Sometime in 2011-12, as a member of a team I had an opportunity to discuss various matters of the Archaeological Survey of India with its Director General. In the light of this discussion we could reach certain conclusions regarding the Survey's policy of archaeological explorations and excavations, conservation policy, administrative policy and publication policy.

The policy of archaeological explorations is characterised by the following features: absence of problem-oriented research and the lack of a proper frame to give training to the archaeological personnel.

Archaeological Survey of India initiated 24 field-programmes in 2011-12. While no comment can be made on this list till some of the results come out in print, one can be sure of one thing: none of these programmes had been undertaken with any specific archaeological problem in mind. To illustrate the nature of such problems, only one or two examples should suffice in the present context. The picture and date of the beginning of early historic phase in the Brahmaputra valley are still hazy. The only evidence of pre-Christian era is available in the form of a 'Sunga bowl' from a surface collection from Tezpur and the presence of a terracotta ring-well in a cliff section at the same site. The Guwahati Circle of the Survey should have no problem in solving this issue but unfortunately this has not yet been attempted. The same list of explorations and excavations for the field-season 2011-12 lists 'prehistoric explorations in Arunachal' as a programme. B.P. Bopardikar of the Survey explored this region from the point of view of prehistoric research many years ago. His claim for the existence of lower palaeolithic tools in the region has been disputed, and for this reason the present programme has some significance, but from the point of view of prehistoric studies in the northeast as a whole, a far more significant programme is to understand in detail the context and chronology of the fossilwood prehistoric industry of Tripura and Mizoram. One also notes that this list of field-programmes includes excavations at Rupar and Patne. Rupar was excavated by Y.D. Sharma in the early 1950s, and it is unlikely that the present excavations will significantly alter the picture of the site. Patne was earlier excavated by S. Sali with interesting results and one cannot follow the logic of re-excavating the site. Further, what is the special justification of re-excavating Raja Vishal Ka Garh at Vaisali? The problem is that the field-programme of the Survey seems to be tied currently to the individual whims of the Circle/ Branch Superintending Archaeologists and not related to the solving of specific cultural issues of different regions or of the country as a whole.

What gives this list a somewhat tragic dimension is that the results of field-programmes mentioned in the list will not be available for many years. The current issue of *Indian Archaeology: A Review*, which is in fact only a brief and summary statement of the archaeological field-researches done in the country in a particular field-season, is dated 2003-04. So, when can one expect this publication bearing the label 2011-12? In how many cases will the concerned archaeologists be caring enough to write full reports of their works?

When one carefully considers these issues, one realizes that the Survey's exploration and excavation programme is often nothing more than a charade.

The Survey's in-house training policy, which is formalized through its 'Institute' (or 'School' as it was known earlier) has so far been a success. In the case of any such Institute, the training programme has to be streamlined from time to time. This may also be accompanied by further specialized trainings (cf. epigraphy, numismatics, specialized branches of archaeological investigations such as prehistory, geomorphology, dating, etc.) in the course of one's career as an officer of the Survey.

The Survey's conservation policy needs approach from several angles. The first is the prioritization of monuments to be conserved in the case of all 'Circles'. This priority list has to be drawn up not on the basis of the relative historical importance of these monuments but on the basis of their present condition and the nature of their conservation problems. The excavated remains of the Amaravati-type stupa site of Kanganahalli near Sannati have been lying in the open in mud for more than a decade. These remains also include the site's priceless sculptures. This should have been among the Survey's topmost conservation priorities. Further, to keep the conservation work in tight leash, the Director General, following an age-old custom of Survey, should frequently visit sites and monuments all over the country and give detailed inspection notes incorporating suggestions to the Circle superintendents and others.

The second conservation issue is more general and relates to the ever-increasing quantum of outsourcing tasks, which have so long been considered the Survey's responsibilities, to various individuals and agencies. This has been going on for quite some time and is leading to the considerable downgrading of the morale of the Survey officers. Measures should be taken to stop such outsourcing to conservation architects and agencies like INTACH. One rarely knows what is done by these conservation architects and INTACH because the concerned architects and INTACH do not usually publish their work.

The third conservation issue is the need to strengthen the chemical wing of the Conservation Branch. The simplest argument in favour of this postulate would be to point out that the paintings of Ajanta have lost their old glow and that the paintings of Sittanavasal have been completely destroyed. The chemical conservators should also be introduced to a range of modern techniques and case studies. For this, the many exchange programmes run by the Government of India, especially with the countries which run extensive research programmes on the conservation of paintings and paper, should be an easy path to follow in the training of the chemical conservators. Further, care should be taken to ensure that there is no wholesale reconstruction of monuments in the name of their conservation.

As far as the Survey's administrative policy is concerned, the primary need is to structure it in such a way that the Survey officers spend more time doing actual archaeology in the field and feel the necessity of writing up the relevant reports. The whole publication machinery should be focussed on this need and the need of expediting the publication of *Indian Archaeology—A Review* on annual basis. Among the other administrative measures, careful attention should be devoted to the strengthening of the Survey's central library and the setting up of a scientific wing for dating and for other analytical purposes. Careful monitoring must be made of the foreign archaeological groups' activities. The recruitment policy should be as transparent as possible.

In a sense, none of the points discussed above is a feature which cannot be easily rectified. For instance, that archaeology field-programmes should be aimed at solving specific cultural issues has long been understood. What prevents their implementation in the field? The answer is simple: general lack of awareness of the cultural and historical issues of the concerned areas and consequently the urge to focus on individual sites alone without appreciating their contexts. It has been equally clear for long that the recovery of archaeological data would also call for various scientific analytical tools. The fact that India still lacks such a scientific support structure is due to a lot of factors including the lack of integration of archaeology as an academic subject in the university academic frame of the country, but there is no reason why the Archaeological Survey of India could not build up an extensive scientific infrastructure for its own fieldwork results. Among other things, is it too much to expect that the Archaeological Survey of India should have an elaborate dating set-up?

Thus, what we encounter is general indifference at every step to the tasks which have to be done in the cultural field. This has got nothing to do with the basic organizational structure which has been built up to handle the cultural affairs of the nation. What has turned out to be more or less catastrophic in this field is the refusal to own up individual responsibilities, as we have pointed out in the case of the performance audits of the five Kolkata and West Bengal organizations. Again, nobody in charge of these leading institutions concerned with culture was apparently prepared to consider national interests in the performance of their regular official duties. In the case of the Archaeological Survey of India also the interest and honour of the nation were nowhere in the picture.

3

Who Owns the Indian Past?

The Case of the Indus Civilization

The question 'who owns the past' is not a rhetorical question. On the one hand, it is tied to the issue of identities, which has played a major role in archaeological research since its very inception, and on the other, it is bound up with the various features of cultural resource management including the thorny relationship between the mainstream archaeology and the rights of indigenous people in the countries like USA, Australia and Canada.

There is a vast amount of literature on both themes. The first one, i.e. the question of identity, is linked to the establishment of national identity as well as various other collective identities like gender, ethnicity and religion. The issue of identity may assume many forms and generate many debates. In the context of Israel and the Palestinian territory, it has been argued[1], for instance, that there are four types of 'desired pasts' there: (1) the Israeli desired past which is sought by the Israeli state and the Jewish organizations of the United States; (2) the conservative Christian past which is championed by the Christian fundamentalist organizations, the American School of Oriental

Research and the Biblical Archaeological Society; (3) the Palestinian desired past, favoured by the Palestinian rights organizations and Palestinian archaeologists and intellectuals; and finally, (4) the diplomatic desired past, as represented by the appointed officials of the US State department.

Issues such as these have always been parts of archaeological research tradition, but in the modern world where the public awareness of such issues is much sharper, archaeological literature has to be concerned with the process and nature of various identity-formations.

The second theme is equally visible, although currently at its sharpest only in the United States and Australia. The Native American Graves Protection and Repatriation Act, a federal law requiring agencies and institutions in receipt of federal funding to return native American human remains, funerary objects, sacred objects and objects of cultural patrimony to their respective peoples, was passed in 1990. Similarly, the recognition of the traditional land-rights of the Australian indigenous people has also led to the recognition of their control over the cultural objects, sacred places and human remains found in their land[2].

The study of the past cannot be said to have ever been free of its socio-politics. Since 1986, when the World Archaeological Congress held its first session in Southampton, the study of this socio-politics has been a part of the mainstream study of the subject. There can never be an one-to-one answer to an archaeological problem, however science-based or logical it may be. In each case, the data are located in a field of uncertainty, however small, and that is filled up by the researcher's own socio-political predilection.

The focus of my present essay is to examine how the different aspects of the Indus civilizational studies have been conditioned by the socio-politics of our attitudes to the Indian past.

I shall begin by taking up the problem of the date of the beginning of this civilization. Many Indian books still refer to the date propounded first in 1946 by Mortimer Wheeler, i.e. 2500 BC. That was based on Wheeler's own subjective estimate of the date of the earliest contact between the Indus Civilization and Mesopotamia. Assuming that this contact was not significantly earlier than the reign of the Mesopotamian king Sargon and accepting 2325 BC as Sargon's date, he arrived at the round figure of 2500 BC, allowing 175-odd years for this civilization to form a relationship with Mesopotamia. The earliest date of the Mesoptamian civilization, typified by the Early Dynastic Period is 2700/2800 BC. Thus, according to Wheeler's scheme, the Indus Civilization was later than the Mesopotamian civilization, which was natural in the light of his belief that the idea of civilization came to the Indus from the former. In 1931 John Marshall thought that the date of Indus-Mesopotamia contact was earlier than the period of Sargon and he arrived, through various subjective calculations, at the date of *c.* 3250 BC for the beginning of the civilization on the Indus. Marshall, who spent his life laying the foundations of Indian archaeology, did not believe that India owed her Bronze Age civilization to any foreign source and thus he had no interest in making it look late in comparison with Mesoptamia and Egypt. By the time Wheeler wrote, India had ceased to be the jewel in the British crown and he had no particular reason to feel enchanted by Indian antiquity.

The modern situation is no less intriguing. After the first crop of radiocarbon dates from the Indus sites, D.P. Agrawal, who, as the Secretary of the Radiocarbon Committee of the Tata Institute of Fundamental Research, had a hand in obtaining some of them, argued that these dates, could not suggest anything earlier than 2400 BC as the date of the beginning of the mature Indus Civilization. He believed that this tallied with Wheeler's opinion that the Indus-Mesopotamia contact did not date before Sargon, forgetting that radiocarbon dates are not historical dates. Agrawal represents some Indian archaeologists of the 1960s and 1970s, who considered it unsafe to go beyond the hitherto accepted framework of Indian archaeology. The premise was that any argument in favour of an earlier Indian past would not be 'scientific' and would more damagingly be termed 'nationalistic'.

The radiocarbon dates kept on coming, and definitive evidence of pre-Sargonic Indus-Mesopotamia contact also emerged. The largest series of the relevant radiocarbon dates emerged from the American excavations at Harappa, and the American interpretation of these dates was that the mature Indus Civilization began around 2600 BC. The American scholars, while interpreting their series of dates, did not even mention the historical profile of Indus-Mesopotamia contact, which was used by earlier scholars. The point is that an archaeologist from the Netherlands, the late ECL During-Caspers, and I demonstrated, independently of each other, that the famous Royal Graves of Ur, which are securely dated about 2600 BC, contained two types of carnelian beads of indisputably Indus manufacture. There could not be a shadow of doubt that there was a trading relationship between the Indus and Mesopotamia by 2600 BC. Assuming that the Indus Civilization must have taken some time before organizing trade with an area as far as Mesopotamia or modern Iraq, I pushed its inception 100 years earlier, and put it at 2700 BC. This date makes the beginnings of the Indus and Mesopotamian civilizations contemporary[3].

Most of the Indian scholars, including Upinder Singh's much-publicised textbook of ancient and early mediaeval India, prefer to cite the American date of 2600 BC. The reason is two-fold: first, unfamiliarity with the primary data and the consequent inability to assess various scholarly opinions critically, and secondly, a marked reluctance to accept an early date for anything Indian in the fear that their names would be associated with the BJP, or worse, with the RSS. My familiarity with the various shades of political opinion among Indian archaeologists convinces me that none of our political parties and organizations has a coherent and professional attitude to the Indian past, archaeological or otherwise. Interestingly, a centre for the study of the Indus Civilization, funded by an American organization called Global Heritage Fund, was proposed to be set up in Vadodara where in the persons of K.K. Bhan and Ajith Prasad who have worked with the Americans, Italians, Spaniards and Japanese with funds coming from the latter, there is already a right kind of situation. The focus has now reputedly shifted to Deccan College, Pune, where the role of Bhan and Prasad in Vadodara has been assumed by Vasant Shinde who also likes to go to the field with assistance from the Americans and the Japanese. It is apparent that the concerned Indians have apparently no idea of how such internationally funded heritage organizations can be used to manipulate the sense of the past in the Third World. Or, even if they are aware of this dimension, they are not simply bothered, as long as they can hope to derive some advantage out of it.[4]

As I began by talking about the date of the beginning of the Indus Civilization, let me talk a bit more about the Indus chronology. How long did it continue? The answer is: 'up to about 1300 BC'. This date is suggested both by the radiocarbon dates and the finds of Indus seals in the Kassite levels of the Mesopotamian site of Nippur. The point is that instead of a thousand-year-old chronology, we have now got a 1400-year-old chronology, and this longer chronology, as we shall see later, has some important implications.

Did this civilization whose full-fledged form dates from *c.* 2700 BC have a prelude or ealier formative stages, and if so, has this evidence been found in the subcontinent? Two sites in Haryana—Kunal and Bhirrana, both near Fatehabad—have shown two such stages, one 'early Harappan', the trace of which has been found at many sites, and second, 'pre-early Harappan' or what scholars call ' the level of the Hakra Ware'. There is no radiocarbon date from Kunal but there are several from Bhirrana, some dating from the 4th, 5th and 6th millennia BC. To be honest, there are some uncertainties regarding their context, but I shall not hesitate to put the beginning of the Hakra Ware level at this site at least in the first half of the 4th millennium BC, possibly closer to 4000 than 3500 BC. Now, if we look at the whole dated profile, we shall realize that the archaeological cultural tradition represented by the Indus Civilization covers really a long and continuous span—a span of about 2500 years (tentatively, 3800 BC as the date of the Hakra level at Bhirrana, and *c.* 1300 BC as the date of the end of the Harappan tradition), if not more.

If the chronological column of the Indus Civilization is, according to my argument, at least 2500-year-long, one of the most obvious inferences is that it was more deeply rooted in the subcontinental soil than we had hitherto been prepared to admit. Secondly, the very fact that this tradition lasted so long, covering virtually the whole area between Jammu and Gujarat and between

Baluchistan and the outer front of the Siwaliks in Panjab, Haryana and western U.P., implies that it interacted with the areas around it. From Gujarat, for instance, the Malwa plain of central India is open, and the western U.P. is inextricably connected with the vast sweep of the Ganga plain. *To argue that the Indus Civilization had no special archaeological bearing on the archaeology of the subcontinent outside its distribution area has no meaning in the geographical sense. Similarly, to speak of a 'Ganga Civilization', completely separate from the Indus Civilization, does not have much meaning either.* In western U.P., between the Yamuna and the Siwaliks, the two traditions are known to have interacted. The occurrence of the Gangetic Valley 'copper hoards' in the otherwise Harappan assemblage of Sinauli near Baghpat is a major evidence of this interaction, and so is the interlocking of the Harappan and Painted Grey Ware levels at Alamgirpur near Meerat. I suspect that the painted pottery that one finds in Bulandshahr and Aligarh at some of the OCP sites is a part of the Harappan tradition, although it is not yet possible to be positive on this issue. One of the outstanding discoveries of the Harappan material in the Ganga Plain is the find of what Dr. Rakesh Tewari of Uttar Pradesh State Archaeological Organization calls a piece of indisputably Harappan perforated vessel in an apparently mixed assemblage in the recent excavations at Ramnagar opposite Varanasi.[5]

There is an attempt in the archaeological literature to disassociate, as far as possible, the Indus Civilization from modern India. J.M. Kenoyer's name for it in his *The Ancient Cities of the Indus Valley Civilization* (Karachi, Oxford University Press) is the 'Indus Valley Civilization', which clearly carries the implication that it is primarily a product of the Indus Valley, all of which is in Pakistan. I find this erroneous term being freely used even in the Indian archaeology journals. I do not know if the Indians who use this term are even aware of its implication. The term 'Indus-Sarasvati Civilization' is also wrong because it takes away the significance of the occurrence of the Indus sites in Gujarat and western U.P. The only logical terms are the Indus Civilization or the Harappan Civilization. The first excavated site of the civilization is Harappa.

Another related feature is the emphasis on what is called 'middle Asian interaction sphere' to explain the growth and appearance of the Indus Civilization. A convenient example of this emphasis is G.Possehl's *The Indus Civilization, a Contemporary Perspective* (Lanham, Maryland 2002: Alta Mira Press). The different kinds of interaction between the different components of the interaction zone between the Indus and the Oxus are well known, but the present archaeological data do not suggest that the growth of the Indus Civilization was due to this interaction. Among other things, this does not take into consideration the implication of the overwhelming number of Indus sites far to the east of the Indus. There is no doubt that the cultural sequence that has been unearthed at Kunal and Bhirrana, or for that matter, at Padri and Dholavira, is way beyond the Indus-Oxus orbit.

After the discovery of Mehrgarh in the Bolan Pass area of Baluchistan, the general tendency in the archaeological literature is to treat the Indus Civilization in a straight arrow-line of development beginning with the growth of wheat-barley agriculture in Baluchistan. Again, Possehl's book, which we have cited above, offers a ready example. The problem is that this notion downgrades, possibly wilfully., the role which the non-wheat-barley agricultural tradition to the east possibly played in the genesis of this civilization. Both rice and millets occur at several Early Harappan and Mature Harappan sites of Haryana and Panjab, including Harappa. These two crops are not known to have been domesticated in Baluchistan. In the central Ganga plain and its Vindhyan fringe, the antiquity of rice cultivation goes back to the 7th millennium BC. The rice that one finds in the Early Harappan Haryana (Balu and Kunal) could have been only of eastern derivation. To relate the growth of the Indus Civilization only to the growth of wheat-barley agricultural tradition in Baluchistan is to imply that the growth of this Civilization is oriented to the West. This assumption ignores the multilineal character of its formation over a singularly large and diverse territory. Related to this trend is the current attempt by an American archaeobotanist to deny the presence of rice cultivation at Lohuradeva in the central Ganga Plain.[6]

A major archaeological fact disputing the notion of an exclusively Western orientation of the Indus Civilization is the growth of early agriculture and metallurgy along the Aravallis in Rajasthan. In my book *The Archaeology of Ancient Indian Cities* in 1995, I pointed out the probable role of the Aravalli metallurgical development in the genesis of the Mature Harappan Civilization, but regrettably, the whole issue has been ignored even by scholars who specialise in Rajasthan. For instance, in V.N. Misra's recent summation of the prehistoric and archaeological data from Rajasthan in his *Rajasthan: Prehistoric and Early Historic Foundations* (Delhi 2007: Aryan Books), there is no mention of this issue. On the other hand, the claim of the Aravalli system as an early and independent centre of agricultural origin is getting increasingly strong. First, we may consider the case of Bagor in Bhilwara. The fact that cattle, sheep and goat of Period I at Bagor were domesticated and the fact that the earliest chronological point of this period falls in the 6th millennium BC suggest the possibility of Bagor–I having an agricultural component. In the next period Bagor yielded copper implements, of which the arrowhead is identical with the arrowhead type of the subsequently excavated site of Ganeshwar, located further up the Aravallis. In its first phase Ganeshwar was exclusively marked by microliths but possessed a number of copper tools in the next phase itself. It has not been generally realized that Bagor and Ganeshwar in two different sections of the Aravallis have the same archaeological sequence. It is likely that Ganeshwar–I and Bagor–I belonged to the same period, i.e. the 6th millennium BC and Ganeshwar also had an agricultural dimension like the latter site. The 6th millennium BC date for the so-called Mesolithic level in the Aravallis has also been highlighted by the mid-6th millennium BC date for a 60 cm thick Mesolithic deposit on the eastern face of Gilund-2 (Bhilwara district where Bagor also is situated). The issue needs further research, but what is intriguing is that the beginning of the chalcolithic occupation at Balathal in the same region has now been found to be about 3700 BC (calibrated). This implies a considerably earlier beginning of agriculture in the region, and as there is no reason to infer that this beginning was due to an infiltration from another area, one has to accept that this suggests an independent beginning of agriculture and metallurgy in the Aravalli zone[7].

The attempts to disassociate the Indus tradition from the later Indian heritage have also taken other forms. Those familiar with John Marshall's discussion on the Indus sculpture in *Mohenjo-daro and the Indus Civilization* (1931) will recall that the entire framework of that discussion was in terms of the 'Indianness' of the relevant specimens, and he worked out this 'Indianness' by pointing out the stylistic and conceptual similarities between the Indus sculptural objects and some examples of later Indian sculptures. It is this postulated link which is being currently questioned.

The famous 'priest-king' head and torso from Mohenjo-daro has been compared first with some specimens from Bactria and then with various other sundry representations from West Asia (cf. Ardeleanu-Jansen). This exercise has been singularly unedifying. Even if one assumes that the priest-king figure was a part of a seated image, the whole concept and representation of this image is completely different from the examples which have been cited from Bactria and other central and West Asiatic places. That the figure suggested the concept of a *Yogi* wrapped in meditation with his eyes fixed on the top of his nose was pointed out in detail by R.P. Chanda soon after its discovery at Mohenjo-daro. The problem with the study of Indus sculptural tradition is that very few specimens have so far been found, and that too primarily from two sites, Mohenjo-daro and Harappa. One gets only occasional flickers of the fact that the spread of the Indus tradition was possibly more deep-rooted and widespread than we admit, in such discoveries as that of a stone monitor lizard or *Godhika* at Dholavira and the incised outline of the Mohenjo-daro 'dancing girl' on a potsherd at Bhirrana. That the iconographic tradition of this civilization was diverse is clear from the representations of sundry human figures on its seals. This tradition is also overwhelmingly 'Indian' in the sense that they can be explained in terms of the later and mostly current ritual beliefs.

This leads us to the question of the Indus religion. Many scholars, both foreign and Indian, are very reluctant to find any trace of modern Hindu rituals and beliefs in the finds which have been interpreted as evidence of Indus religion. Two facts, however, cannot be wished away—regrettably from the point of view of this group of people. One is the indubitable presence of

Siva in the form of *linga*-like stones found both at Mohenjo-daro and Harappa, a distinctively phallic stone column at Dholavira, a seated ithyphallic stone figure from the same site, the famous 'Siva-Pasupati' figure on a seal, and the terracotta representation of a *Sivalinga* set in *Yonipatta* at Kalibangan. The second such evidence is the widespread presence of sacrificial pits at Lothal, Kalibangan, Banawali, Rakhigarhi and possibly a few other sites. These pits possibly have variations of their own. Their shapes and contents may also vary from site to site. However, their generic similarity with the 'havan kundas' which many devout people still dig up every day, light fire in, and pour offerings on, is undeniable.

Again, one has only to look up the section on religion in *Mohenjo-daro and the Indus Civilization* to find the footprints of later day Hinduism in the ruins of the Indus Civilization. I shall not argue that Hinduism in its modern forms flourished there. All that I would say that the roots of some major Hindu religious beliefs and rituals can be traced back to that period. As far as the early scholars were concerned, that was obvious. Even to people like me, that is the most simple and straightforward explanation of the category of artefacts which have been found at the Indus sites and can be associated with religion and ritual beliefs. Doubts have been expressed in the modern context because there are scholars who will not like to see the continuation of Hinduism in any form from this early period.

In a small but important volume entitled *The Sarasvati Flows On: the Continuity of Indian Culture*, (Delhi: Aryan Books, 2002), the seniormost archaeologist of the country, B.B. Lal, has offered an outline of the various traits of Indian behaviour which have continued from the protohistoric times to the present. Even outside this book some major examples can be given. For instance, one has only to look up the list of the plant-remains found at the Indus sites to realize that the agricultural pattern of the subcontinent has been reflected in that list. The general idea is that the Indus people were not familiar with irrigation and depended on the over-bank floods of the Indus to sow their crops. There was certainly some dependence on the river floods of the rivers during that period, but a far more probable hypothesis in the light of modern but pre-industrial agricultural practices in Sindh is that canal irrigation was used. The practice of both double-cropping and irrigation was there, and I have been trying to argue this since 1988 *(Theroretical Issues in Indian Archaeology*, Delhi 1988: Munshiram Manoharlal) but without any effect on the mindset of Indus specialists. Regarding Harappan technology, especially regarding Harappan metal technology, it has been convincingly argued by Nayanjot Lahiri that the preference for pure copper products in the range of Harappan metal objects may be explained by the general preference for ritually pure copper materials in modern India[8]. The point is that it is no reflection on the technological status of Harappan metallurgy that many of its specimens were unalloyed.

In the general field of Indus technological studies, a noteworthy development in recent years is to analyse the technical skills involved in various crafts by employing village craftsmen to replicate them. The knowledge imparted by the traditional craftsmen is couched in terms of modern science, and by the time the process results in publications, the village craftsmen are forgotten and in their place we find modern 'western' scientists trying to lay down laws on the Indus crafts. This tendency has become dominant after the American excavations at Harappa under Kenoyer. Such studies are no doubt useful but provide an excellent example of how the traditional crafts of the subcontinent can be appropriated by 'western science'.

At this point, it may be apt to point out how the study of the Indus Civilization itself is being appropriated by 'western science'. In June 2008, the American magazine *Science* published a lengthy article in several sections on the Indus Civilization. The sections numbered six and carried the following headings: (1) Unmasking the Indus: boring no more, a trade-savvy Indus emerges; (2) Unmasking the Indus: Buddhist stupa or Indus temple?; (3) Unmasking the Indus: Indus collapse: the end or the beginning of an Asian culture? (4) Understanding the Indus: trench warfare: modern borders split the Indus; (5) Understanding the Indus: trying to make way for the old; (6) Unmasking the Indus: Pakistani archaeology faces issues old and new.

As excavators two Indian names—V. Shinde and R.S. Bisht, both well-known associates of the American scholars G. Possehl and J.M. Kenoyer—and three Pakistani names–Qasid Mallah, Farzand Massih and G.M. Veesar—have been cited; otherwise the essay cites as 'scholars' only Americans. The title of the sections is, to us, academically meaningless. That the Indus Civilization was, as the writer put it, 'trade-savvy' has been known since its discovery and in 1931 its internal and external trade were comprehensively discussed. That there is a possibility of finding an Indus religious place below the ruins of the Buddhist stupa in the northeastern corner of the western mound of Mohenjo-daro was pointed out as early as 1931. The issue of the Indus decline has also been discussed for ages. That Indian and Pakistani archaeologists do not work together is well known, but to put the record straight, there is no 'trench warfare' between them. Research is a continuous process, and one is not sure why 2008 should mark a point when old ideas regarding the Indus are giving way to the new. Archaeologists anywhere face both old and new issues, and one does not understand the reason of particular emphasis with reference to Pakistani archaeologists. The article states that Mehrgarh was the precursor of the Indus Civilization and that the Indus cities at 2600 BC were 600 years later than those of Mesopotamia, simply forgetting to mention the fact that some early Harappan settlements dating from before 3000 BC were fortified, planned and could be considered cities, especially in view of the fact that the Indus writing had made its appearance by then. Equally interestingly, he approvingly cites the Italian archaeologist G. Verardi's idea that the Buddhist stupa at the northeastern corner of the western mound at Harappa was not a stupa but only a series of platforms on the model of the Sumerian ziggurat, an idea which fits perfectly with Wheeler's idea that there was a strong Mesopotamian impetus to the growth of the Indus Civilization. Incidentally, this stupa structure was investigated by two of India's foremost early archaeologists, R.D. Banerjee and D.R. Bhandarkar, and I have no reason to believe that they did not recognize a Buddhist stupa when they saw one.

Most amazingly, considering that the articles figured in *Science*, the author, A. Lawler, allowed himself some comments on the domestic politics of India:

> The rise of Hindu nationalism in today's India has thrust this scholarly debate into the political spotlight. Hindu nationalists' push to see the roots of their religion in the 5000-year-old Indus civilization creates another barrier between Indian archaeologists and their mostly Muslim counterparts in Pakistan.... The Bharatiya Janata Party (BJP) which ruled India from 1998 to 2004 declared the Indus to be progenitor of Hindu civilization, a controversial claim in a country with a large Muslim

> population. While in power, BJP pumped additional funding into Indus-related digs, and its influence over archaeological matters remains strong.

I agree with the last part of the author's comment. The BJP's influence over Indian archaeological matters must be strong because otherwise how an American-funded Indus Centre with J.M. Kenoyer on board is being set up in Gujarat with the support of its BJP government? Regarding the author's statement that the BJP "declared the Indus to be progenitor of Hindu Civilization", all that one can point out is that it is not usual for any political party in India to declare anything as the progenitor of any aspect of the Indian civilization, nor are they known to make such statements. Lawler's political comments go deeper. Citing Bisht's 'opinion' that the Indus people were 'one and the same with the Aryans', he writes that this 'theory finds little support among foreign scholars'. This attempt to put Indian scholarship vis-à-vis foreign scholarship has long been an important ingredient of Western scholarship on ancient India.

The idea that the Indus Civilization could bear an echo of the Vedic tradition has taken deeper roots in the recent period after it was understood that the densest distribution of the Indus Civilization sites was not along the Indus but along the Hakra which was a part of a river-system parallel to that of the Indus. This river-system has been known to modern scholarship since the late 18th century, and the Ghaggar-Hakra was identified with the Vedic Sarasvati by the French historical geographer L. Vivien de Saint-Martin (1802–1896) possibly in 1860 in his book on the study of the Vedic geography. By 1830, the general archaeological potential of its valley was also understood. The idea that the Indus Civilization and the Vedic tradition could not have been poles apart was perfectly acceptable to scholars like R.P. Chanda, M.S. Vats, B.N. Datta and possibly most significantly, P.V. Kane. They did not discuss the issue from the point of view of modern politics. I do not know the political opinion of Chanda and Vats, but B.N. Datta was one of the forerunners of communist movement in India and, hopefully, P.V. Kane, *Bharatratna*, will not be accused of being a 'Hindu nationalist'. According to Datta, "in religious matters, the present-day Hindus are the descendants of the Indus valley people". Kane, in fact, wrote that the Rigvedic people were earlier than the Indus valley people" and that there was some evidence to believe that the Indus Valley people "were probably Aryans " or different but "contemporaneous with the Rigveda Aryans". I have cited these scholars only to show that the problem was not always tinged with political implications as it is now[9].

People who are very keen to insert a phase of Aryan invasions between the Indus Civilization and the later historic India would prefer to view Hinduism as Aryan in inspiration. This would mean, by implication, that Hinduism is as much native to the Indian soil as the much later immigrant religions like Islam and Christianity. If this belief gives a section of Indian people and what Lawler calls 'foreign scholars', happiness and peace, they are welcome to it. However, this should not be a deterrent on viewing the formative phase of Indian history in the light of the increasingly supportive archaeological data that there is no break in the continuity of Indian archaeological record since prehistory. As I wrote in 2004, "all the people of the subcontinent are, in one way or another, the inheritors of the Indus civilization"[10]. The Indian past represented by this civilization belongs to them.

I conclude this essay by pointing out a danger which is increasingly facing Indian archaeology today. If one goes through the archaeological literature on Egypt and Mesopotamia, the areas where Western scholarship has been paramount since the beginning of archaeological research in those areas, one notes that the contribution made by the native Egyptian and Iraqi archaeologists is completely ignored in that literature. The Bronze Age past of Egypt, Mesoptamia and the intervening region is completely appropriated by the Western scholarship. Also, when Western archaeologists write on Pakistani archaeology, they seldom mention the contribution made by the Pakistani archaeologists themselves. There are exceptions but they are very rare. After Independence, the Archaeological Survey of India pursued a policy of relative isolation, which enabled archaeology as a subject to develop in the country and helped Indian archaeologists to find their feet. The policy seems to be changing now, and supercilious articles like the one by Lawler are an indication of the effect of this change. There is a great deal of arrogance and sense of superiority in that segment of the First World archaeology which specializes in the Third World. Unless this segment of the First World archaeology changes its way and attitude, it should be treated with a great deal of caution in the Third World.

As a British author, William Dalrymple, possibly well known in Delhi, is supposed to have commented in an interview to the Channel 4 of the British television, "One should protect one's own history and fight for it by tooth and claw, as others will always try to change it".

PS. An important point that I have made in this paper is that there is a complete appropriation of the Bronze Age past of

Egypt, Mesopotamia and the intervening region by the Western scholarship. This also includes Pakistan where the Western scholars, even while writing on Pakistan archaeology, seldom mention the contribution made by the Pakistani archaeologists themselves.

This point has recently been driven home once again by what is reported of the Indus Civilization in *Science* under the heading "the ingredients for a 4000-year-old proto-curry" (20 JULY 2012 VOL 337 SCIENCE www.sciencemag.org). The occasion is the identification of cooked ginger and turmeric in human teeth at Farmana and of banana phytoliths from the same site. The author of the note, A. Lawler, does not mention it, but the first item of the ingredient of a curry in the Indus context was reported by an Indian worker, K.S. Saraswat, and it was fenugreek or *methi*, from Kunal. One is surprised by Lawler's emphasis on the occurrence of rice at Masudpur because rice was found much earlier at Kunal and Balu by the same Indian worker. The fact which possibly makes Masudpur rice significant from Lawler's point of view is that it was identified by a (white) Cambridge archaeologist with the name Bates ! He also makes a great deal of the point that Bates' work suggests that both summer and winter cropping were practised by the Masudpur people. The point that the Harappans prastised double-cropping was made by a (brown/ black) Cambridge archaeologist with the name Chakrabarti in 1988 in his book *Theoretical Issues in Indian Archaeology*.

NOTES AND REFERENCES

1. Sandra Scham. Diplomacy and Desired Pasts. *Journal of Social Archaeology* 9(2), 2009: 163-99.
2. Cf. N. Ferries. Between Colonial and Indigenous Archaeologies: Legal and Extra-Legal Ownership of the Archaeological Past in

North America. *Canadian Journal of Archaeology* 27(2), 2003: 154-90; D. Ritchie, Principles and Practice of Site Protection Laws in Australia. In D. Charmichael, J. Hubert, B. Reeves, and A. Schanche (eds.), *Sacred Sites, Sacred Places.* London, 1994: Routledge, pp. 227-44.

3. There is a detailed discussion on Harappan chronology with a historiographical survey of the various estimates and their basis in D. Chakrabarti, *The Archaeology of the Ancient Indian Cities*. Delhi 1995: Oxford University Press.
4. The details of the proposed Indus Centre can be easily located in the web-pages of 'Global Heritage Fund'.
5. For the archaeological details, D. Chakrabarti, *The Oxford Companion to Indian Archaeology*. Delhi 2006: Oxford University Press; I owe my information on the interlocking of Harappan and Painted Grey Ware levels at Alamgirpur to Dr. R.N. Singh of BHU, and I owe my information on the find of a Harappan perforated ware vessel at Ramnagar to Dr. Rakesh Tewari, Director of U.P. State Archaeology.
6. Regarding Lohuradeva rice, the following is the comment of Dorian Fuller in 'archaeobotanist blog', section: Indian archaeobotany watch: Lohuradewa 2008: "I now doubt even more, that the rice was domesticated. It is not even clear that it was cultivated, and is plausibly (perhaps safest interpreted as) wild gathered". Among other things, rice occurs at the site in the 7th-6th millennia BC context as plastering material in mud plaster. Those who have seen the practice in modern Indian villages will know that this practice itself implies a long and close familiarity with rice agriculture. Is there any context where wild rice occurs extensively in mud plaster?
7. The data are cited in detail in D. Chakrabarti, *The Oxford Companion to Indian Archaeology* (Delhi 2006: Oxford University Press).

8. N. Lahiri. Indian Metal and Metal-related Artefacts as Cultural Signifiers: An Ethnographic Perspective. *World Archaeology* 27 (1) 1995, pp. 116-32.
9. This literature has been surveyed in D. Chakrabarti, *The Battle for Ancient India*. Delhi 2008: Aryan Books.
10. D. Chakrabarti (ed.). *Indus Civilization Sites in India: New Discoveries*. Mumbai 2004: Marg Publications.

4

Whose Past and Which Past?

The Warring Factions of the Ancient Indian Historical Research

For about three decades, the politics of the past has been an important part of the theoretical literature of archaeology and ancient studies. One of the earliest books on the topic, *The Socio-politics of Archaeology* (Gero, Laacy and Blakey 1983), was published in 1983, although the publications increased vastly in number only in the wake of the World Archaeology Congress marred by the Apartheid controversy in 1986. This academic theme is now diverse and firmly entrenched in various forms in the syllabi of many Western university departments of Archaeology. In the United States of America and Australia its link-up with the archaeological rights of the Native Americans and Aborigines is strong. There is also a clear concern for the 'socio-politics and the archaeology of the Black Americans' (Franklin 1997). Apart from two books by the present author (Chakrabarti 1997, 2008) and a collection of essays (Chakrabarti 2009), there has been no expression of academic interest in this theme in Indian archaeology. No Indian university offers its systematic study. The Ayodhya affair generated—and still generates—its own political literature, but even in this case a dispassionate academic review of this literature is yet to be attempted. The purpose of the present paper is to outline how and why the study of ancient India including its archaeology has come to be related to different power structures and ideologies which have dominated the Indian scene from the beginning of the British rule to the present.

On the most basic level, the controversy is about the position of India in the scheme of world civilizations. Has it ever been an original and innovative centre of technology and other material traits of life outside the domain of religion and philosophy ? Till the middle of the nineteenth century there was hardly any controversy about it. The European traders had been in India since the early sixteenth century, and if initially the scene was dominated by the Portuguese, the merchants of other nationalities became prominent with varying degrees of success from the beginning of the seventeenth century. Along with the merchants and missionaries came the travellers whose accounts form the most dependable factual narrative of the peoples' life in Mughal India. What is also clear from these accounts is that the texts like the Vedas, Upanishads, etc. were not forgotten and that there was a sense of India's ancient past. Around the middle of the eighteenth century there was also some concern with the objective study of ancient Indian monuments. The place of India among the old civilizations of the world was implicitly accepted by this period. In 1800-1801, Thomas Maurice published a seven-volume study of *Indian Antiquities*. A common opinion of the day was that there was a migration of Brahmins or Buddhist monks as far west as Scotland and the Scottish megaliths were attributed to its impact. When the British rule was firmly established around the middle of the nineteenth century, India including its megaliths came to be viewed at the receiving end of migrations from the west (for the details, Chakrabarti 1976).

In the middle of the nineteenth century F. Max Müller who wrote contemptuously and patronisingly of Indians (for the details, Chakrabarti 1997) provided the image of an inwardly turned India. Although in his *The Wonder That Was India: A Survey of the Culture of the Indian Sub-continent before the Coming of the Muslims* (1954), A.L. Basham, who was infinitely more decent than Max Müller in his attitude to India and Indians, tried to maintain a balance between spirituality and religion and what he described as 'humanity', he did not question any of the deep-rooted assumptions regarding ancient India in his book. The image of the other worldliness of India persists strongly even in the contemporary world. If anything related to India is a relatively popular field of study in the Western universities, that is Indian religion and philosophy. In the British universities at least the historical study of ancient India is more or less defunct. There is a handful of archaeology groups but none with orthodox, or even competent concerns for ancient Indian history. The case of the Department of South Asia in the School of Oriental and African Studies (London), which was the home ground of Basham and many Indian Ph.D. students, is a convenient example. Its website declares the following:

"The research interests of the Department's members include: Vedic texts and Sanskrit epics; Islam in South Asia; nationalism and linguistic identity; medieval Hindu devotional texts; twentieth century fiction in South Asian languages; postcolonial literatures; Bengali, Hindi, Nepali and Urdu poetry; Indian cinema and popular cultures; the South Asian diaspora ; Sikh history and literature; Mughal history; and translation."

Speaking of the interests of the Indian diaspora in Britain, it may be pointed out that whenever it decided to donate some funds for Indian studies in the universities, the selected field was almost invariably a course of lecture/seminar in Indian religion and philosophy. The diaspora is simply not interested in any professional study of the history of ancient India. I have come across a couple of coin-collectors and art-collectors among the diaspora, and there may be more of them. However, the study of ancient Indian history is hardly their concern. The coins and art-objects have their own market values.

Before we regret the dwindling of professional concern with the study of ancient India in Britain or elsewhere in the West, we might look at its present status in India. A proper appraisal of its status in the framework of Indian university and school education will depend on a close study of all the relevant data, which can be attempted possibly only under the aegis of the Indian UGC. What I offer here is what I have experienced in the course of a long university teaching career (1965–2008). The first point to remember in this context is that the Departments of History that we find in different UGC- sponsored institutions in different parts of India are dominated by the study of 'modern India'. All that one has to do is to look at the proportion of teachers with specializations in ancient/mediaeval/modern India in these departments. Or, if one prefers, one may look at the number of research grants/fellowships awarded in the field of ancient India by the Indian Council of Historical Research and compare this number with the total number of research grants sanctioned in other historical fields. Another point worthy of notice is that even in the field of modern India, there is an increasing emphasis on the historical study of mostly contemporary Indian politics. The dominant part of historical studies in modern India does not, in any case, go beyond the coming of the Europeans to India. The place of ancient India in this institutional scheme is marginal. Whereas the study of modern India has by now reached a high professional level, as is evidenced by the range of publications and the basic well-researched character of the articles published in *The Indian Economic and Social History Review*, the study of ancient India in contrast seems to have reached a dead-end in which the repetition of the old theories and miscellaneous scholarly opinions seems to be the primary rule. There is hardly any systematic or enthusiastic concern to re-examine what has been considered sacrosanct in this field so far. There is also no attempt to distinguish between bad scholarship and good scholarship. Many of the Ph.D. theses produced in the field of ancient India in the Indian universities are mostly a rehash of the earlier material and theories. This is an unfortunate academic cycle. On the one hand, because of the low position of the study of ancient India in Indian educational institutions, it generally does not attract bright students and on the other hand, because of the general absence of bright students in the field, the research it generates is mediocre and often despicable.

One of the reasons for this state of affairs is the average Indian concern for the 'usefulness' of a subject in modern commercial terms. What do they teach you in your MA in Ancient India that you will find useful in your job in bank, commercial places, etc ? This attitude has in fact harmed the cause of all 'classical' studies in the country. *The concept of liberal education is unknown in the market places of India, and whatever homage an average Indian middle class person may pay to 'the glory of ancient India', that need not be taken seriously.* His/her notion of the glory of ancient India will not, in any case, extend much beyond the long-bearded sages that one finds in the illustrations of *Amar Chitra Katha.*

The recent emphasis of a section of expatriate or non-Resident Indians on the hidden or unexplored depths of Indian wisdom in the Vedas, etc. is a part of this insubstantial Indian middle class intellectual tradition. This emphasis is formally structured as 'World Association of Vedic Studies' and its 'articles of incorporation, Article IV' list among its objectives the following: "to promote Vedic and ancient Indian studies in all its forms". For its conference in August 4-7, 2010 in Trinidad-Tobago, it called for papers on a wide variety of themes.

"Papers will include topics on archaeology and anthropology, history and social sciences, language, literature and linguistics, science and technology, Vedas, Upanishads, Smritis, Puranas, epics—*Ramayana* and *Mahabharata, Gita*, contemporary works and issues, Dharmasastras, ethics and rituals, agriculture, plant science and ecology, interreligious dialogue, health, yoga and martial arts, business, economics and administration, etc."

Interestingly, the website of the 'Greater Atlanta Vedic Temple Society' states that it was established in 1986 to "teach Vedic civilization and its philosophy" and that in October 1996 it hosted a conference on "re-visiting Indus Civilization and ancient India" with emphasis on such topics as 'myth of Aryan invasion' and 'distortions regarding Hindu religion as taught in the US schools'.

There is apparently a similarity in the declared objectives of both these groups, but when 'the myth of Aryan invasion' is among the declared items of a 'Vedic temple society' conference, or when there is conference on everything from Indian archaeology to yoga and martial arts, one has reasons to feel worried about the professionalism of such 'associations' or 'societies'. Incidentally, the very idea of Aryans is a racist myth, as I argued in my *Colonial Indology*, and one need not expect Western Indology to be anything but superciliously arrogant and racist in relation to Hinduism, as K. Ramaswamy, A.D. Nicolas and A. Banerjee (2007) have shown in their edited volume *Invading the Sacred: An Analysis of Hinduism Studies in America*, but here I am only commenting on the undesirable link-up between one's religious preference and belief and a subject like archaeology.

As far as archaeology, perhaps the most important component of ancient Indian studies in post-Independence India, is concerned, the following comment made by me in *Organizer* of February 28, 2010 in the context of the recent selection of the Archaeological Survey of India's Director General may clarify the general picture.

> The websites of the Ministry of Culture, Government of India, and one of its subordinate offices, the Archaeological Survey of India, cannot be accused of attaching any special significance to archaeological research. The 'mission statement' of the Ministry refers to only the "maintenance and conservation of heritage, historic sites and ancient monuments", and following this, the Archaeological Survey announces that the "maintenance of ancient monuments and archaeological sites and remains of national importance" is its 'primary concern'.
>
> From this official point of view, the Archaeological Survey of India is not a research or academic body. It is essentially a maintenance organisation on the model of the PWD. Whereas the PWD is concerned only with the construction and maintenance of modern structures, the Archaeological Survey of India's focus is on the maintenance and preservation of historic sites and

> monuments. We should soon get rid of the notion that the Archaeological Survey and its State level counterparts are supported by the Government to advance the academic cause of archaeology. After all, in very few countries of the modern world the governments would take the direct responsibility of conducting archaeological research. That research has played only a minor part in the Archaeological Survey's post-Independence agenda is also clear from the sheer number of the unpublished explorations and excavations done by it.

Very few Indian universities offer archaeology. They are also fairly unenthusiastic about their approach to archaeological research. I know one full-fledged university archaeology department which, since its establishment in 1960, has only published the result of its first year of excavations in 1962. I know another university department—a Department of Ancient Indian History, Culture and Archaeology—where the results of excavations of a major Harappan site are not merely unpublished beyond a few pages but also the entire pottery collection from the site was reputedly taken out of the pottery bags and their contents were mixed up and buried in the trenches specifically dug for the purpose. The scientific back-up of the subject remains marginal in the country. The government is simply not bothered about setting up a national laboratory for archaeological dating and chemical and other analyses. Even the quality of the Ajanta paintings has been allowed to be compromised. I would say that the present state of affairs in Indian archaeology also shows, as the present state of affairs in the study of ancient India in the Indian universities does, that 'ancient India' does not figure conspicuously in the Indian middle class vision. Paying homage to the Vedas is unlikely to bring about any change in this vision.

If the expatriate organization called WAVES could raise money for setting up a laboratory for dating and material analyses instead of moaning over the Vedas, we could perhaps think more respectfully of their concern for ancient India. The whole set-up can be made on a strictly commercial basis, with the laboratory charging a cost-effective fee for every sample submitted to it.

The preoccupation of a large number of people with the various imagined mysteries of the Sarasvati River is also a part of this Veda-centred orientation. There is nothing mysterious about this river, the course of which was known to the geographers as early as the late eighteenth century. A survey of its drainage system from the Siwaliks to the Arabian Sea was conducted at the ground level around this time—before 1790, as H.G. Raverty points out. The survey remained unpublished but was used extensively by Raverty who wrote more than a 500-page-long article on this, utilizing extensively the major mediaeval sources, between the 9th and 13th centuries and showing, on that impeccable historical basis, that the river system was alive right up to the 14th century. As it has been pointed out in a review of Raverty's opinion,

"In the 14th century, the Hakra continued to be a perennial stream, although it lost a lot of water due to the desertion of the Indus and other Panjab rivers except the Sutlej. According to Raverty this was the general situation till the Mughal invasion in the 16th century" (Chakrabarti and Saini 2009, p. 19)

This is supported by an inscriptional reference to 'eastern Sarasvati' near Pehoa in the 10th century. The roughly contemporary literary sources speak warmly of the richness of the well-irrigated Yaudheya country, i.e. the area of modern Haryana and the Indian section of modern Panjab. Where was this irrigation water coming from unless it came from the river-system of the region ? In fact, if one consults the late nineteenth century district gazetteers of Haryana, one realizes that flood water sustained sufficient agricultural production in many places (for the details, Chakrabarti and Saini 2009). The scientific study of a dried-up river system has an academic rigour of its own, especially when the satellite imageries have opened up a wide array of drainage lines over a vast area from the Siwaliks to the sea. The growth of human settlements in the region deserves close analysis too. We must be thankful to Dr. Kalyanaraman for drawing our attention to the various types of research available currently on the Sarasvati in his famous website on this river.

There is nothing to get excited about the early literary references to the Sarasvati, all of which have been objectively summarized in M. Danino's recently published book (Danino 2010). Regrettably, no great historical conclusion can be reached on that basis. However, if the Sarasvati was ever a river full of rushing water throughout her course, that must denote a period before the Mature Indus Civilization had come into existence about 2700 BC. The isotopic study of the ground water for about a 100-km-stretch of the Hakra in Bahawalpur has its dates between 11000 and 2700 BC, suggesting that this ground water was not recharged after *c.* 2700 BC, i.e. the end of the Early Harappan period. Another work of this kind in western Rajasthan along the dried-up bed of a river probably linked to the Sarasvati system suggests that the concerned water-table has not been replenished since *c.* 3000 BC (for the details, Danino 2010). There are many problem areas of research, but if the available dates are dependable, the river seemingly went into decline as early as the first half of the third millennium BC. The Rigvedic references to its flowing character have to be earlier than this date, and if it upsets Max Müller's date of the *Rigveda*, one does not have to feel worried. I have pointed out how in 1953, P. Kane wrote that some parts of the *Rigveda* could date from the sixth-fifth millennia BC and how in his history of Indian literature M.Winternitz pointed out that there was no way the date of the *Rigveda* could be pegged to a fixed point (for the details, Chakrabarti 2008). A lot of archaeological and scientific research has to be done in the Sarasvati Basin before major cultural conclusions can be reached.

I have suggested two main points so far. First, there is no significant spread of professional research interest either in ancient Indian history or in archaeology in modern India. Secondly, in some quarters this has combined with enthusiasm to correlate some of our religious traditions with the emerging archaeological data from the Sarasvati Valley and to try to convince ourselves that the Vedas constituted a major source of historical knowledge.

But there are also people to whom the very mention of Indian tradition is redolent of an unacceptably Hindu India. From this point of view, the Sarasvati has to be argued as a mythical river and Hinduism has to be interpreted as a phenomenon which developed only after the Aryans came to India. From this perspective, Hinduism is as much native to the Indian soil as Islam and Christianity are. All of them came with the influx of new people, the Aryans in the case of the Hindus, the Muslims in the case of Islam and the Europeans in the case of Christianity. The idea of continuity of the Indian civilization does not suit the beliefs of this group of people.

There is a serious difference between these two groups. Whereas you can laugh the opinions of the former group away as those of Hindu traditionalists, you cannot do that in the case of the latter for the simple reason that they are mostly Government of India historians with powers over the fate of history students and teachers in the country. India may be the only country where the government has its own brand of historians by appointing them in various capacities to the Indian Council of Historical Research which controls virtually the entire funding of historical research in the country. Irfan Habib, to whom the name Sarasvati is a kind of anathema, was a former chairman of this organization directly under the Ministry of Culture/Education. Habib (2001) has his faith in an obscure nineteenth century opinion (Thomas 1883) that the name Sarasvati was originally given to the Helmand River in Afghanistan and that was later transferred to the one near Kurukshetra in Haryana. This opinion which was ignored by people like C.F. Oldham and Aurel Stein (for the details, Chakrabarti and Saini 2009) seems to have found favour among some modern Sanskritists (cf. Hock 2000) and Government of India historians like Habib. The problem with the historical linguists and those who have faith in historical linguists/ comparative philology is that they apparently inhabit a world in which there is no need for independently testing a theory. One would, however, have thought that Habib as a historian would critically examine the source on which the idea that the Helmand was the original Sarasvati was based.

In any case, the Sarasvati-phobia of this group of scholars is inexplicable. If they are upset by the density of distribution of Harappan sites in the region drained by the Sarasvati and get alarmed by the prospect of the Indus Civilization being associated with ancient Brahmavarta, basically the land between the Sarasvati and the Drishadvati, that is their problem. The problem is in no case a simple one. If the origin of the Indus Civilization was in that holy stretch of land called the Brahmavarta, the possibility of its being associated with the people of early Indian texts becomes very strong indeed. Assuming that these people were 'Aryans', the link between the Indus Civilization and the Aryans becomes strong too. This also seems to nullify the notion that these people behind the early Indian texts, i.e. the Aryans, were not indigenous. In other words, there could not have been any Aryan invasion.

Unfortunately this opens a very large can of worms. How does it matter if no mythical group of warriors called the Aryans had not appeared in the Indian scene? Why should we be so keen on locating the Aryan homeland in India or on locating it wherever we prefer to locate it outside India? How is it that the post-Independence Indian archaeology has been dominated by the Aryan hypothesis? Even a cursory review of the way the Aryan idea has been built up, which I tried to do in *Colonial Indology*, will point out that the whole idea is intimately related to racism without any empirical existence of its own. The fact that a large number of archaeologists have come round to the belief that there is no archaeological evidence of Aryan invasion in India need not fill the heart of Hindu traditionalists with delight because on the other side, there is no archaeological evidence to show that India was sending out the Aryans anywhere. However, this does not deter scholars like R.S. Sharma to write books on the 'advent of Aryans' in India or B.B. Lal to argue in his book on the Aryan homeland that India sent the Aryans outside. In the 1950s it was B.B. Lal who in his *Ancient India* report on Hastinapura argued that the Painted Grey Ware was associated with the Mahabharata period and the coming of the Aryans to India. Such theories caused damage to the cause of archaeological studies in the country because it is not the business of archaeology to seek the validity of literary tradition. On the contrary, if it has to justify its academic existence, it must try to offer a comprehensive archaeological history of the land. The idea that the Painted Grey Ware was an Aryan pottery has caused considerable damage to the study of ancient Indian history in north India because two or three generations of students who were raised on a strong diet of this theory in the many books written for them in Hindi accepted this idea almost as an axiom. Similarly, the idea that the Aryan homeland was India should be discarded forthwith. To harp on the 'glory of ancient India', one does not have to brandish it as the Aryan homeland. One should have enough faith in one's country without this kind of mumbo-jumbo. D.D. Kosambi, an Indian communist icon to whom it is almost obligatory for Government of India historians to pay homage, went to the extent of calling Painted Grey Ware 'Puru-Kuru ceramics'.

'Mumbo-jumbo' is a word I shall cheerfully apply also to the notion that the ancient Tamil land has almost a birth-right to the Indus Civilization. First, who has asked us to assume that there was a single language in the Indus belt which extended from Baluchistan/Iran border to the Siwaliks of Panjab, Haryana and western UP? Do the people of this vast region speak in one language now? Secondly, even without the Indus Civilization, the ancient Tamil country has a lot to be proud of. Among other things, this was the most important steel-manufacturing region of the country. Its early historic antiquity is also on par with most of the other parts of the country. Megaliths and Roman coins happen to be two umbilical cords of south Indian archaeology, and the sooner these cords are cut and south Indian archaeology allowed to drift beyond the megaliths and Romans the better. I may note that under the inspiring initiative of K. Rajan the Tamil Nadu archaeology has already taken steps in this direction(cf. Rajan, Yathees Kumar and Selvakumar 2009).

The foregoing preoccupations dealing with the study of ancient Indian past are primarily methodological pre-occupations. They do not, however, tell the full story. The second sub-area of dispute is the extent to which the different technological elements like food-production, metallurgy, etc. are the results of diffusionary spreads or indigenous developments. Also, in almost all spheres of the Indus Civilization we have encountered such disputes, including those about its chronology, continuity, etc. We cannot come to straight conclusions about many of these issues but we can surely show that the situation is more complex than is usually admitted.

To begin with, the case of the beginning of food-production in the subcontinent is an important example. Basically there are multiple strands of early development, based around the major cereals like wheat-barley, rice and millets. My assessment of the current archaeological situation in the Aravallis (cf. Chakrabarti 2006, pp. 225-234) suggests that it was an early centre of agriculture. In the second edition of my book *India: An Archaeological History* (2009, p. 346), I wrote that "the claim of the Aravalli system as an early and independent centre of agricultural origin is getting increasingly strong". This hypothesis has since then been proved by Arunima Kashyap's evidence of use-wear and starched-grain analysis of the microliths from both the aceramic and ceramic phases of Bagor (cited by V. Shinde 2008. Cultural development from Mesolithic to Chalcolithic in the Mewar region of Rajasthan, India, *Pragdhara* 18 201-213; this publication by Shinde was not available to me when I published my studies mentioned above.) shows the use of a root-crop like ginger and other plants like sesame, horse-gram, date-palm and mango in the aceramic phase (5700–4500 BC) and the further use of tamarind, pigeon-pea, barley, ragi millet and jowar millet in the ceramic phase (4500–3500 BC).

The dates (4990–2080 BC) from Dandak and Kotumsar caves of Bastar (Yadava et al. 2007) and their association with fire, two varieties of millets and three varieties of grass, all of which have their modern-day uses, demonstrate the multiple and varied transitions to agricultural way of life in various parts of India. The trajectory of early agricultural development is a complex archaeological and scientific issue, but in the Indian context this has begun to be messed up by trying to associate this with miscellaneous language groups. Although known for a long time, this approach, which has re-emerged recently in places like Cambridge, London and Canberra, has to be considered puerile because there is no independently tested way of associating a language group with a specific cultural trait. Besides, such claims have strong political tones which a country like India, which has some major language-families, cannot afford to have. The Third World countries, especially the multi-ethnic and multi-language ones, would do themselves well by being very wary of this approach. What I personally have always failed to understand is why in the history of archaeology there has been so much concern with identifying cultural data with language groups without a clear and acceptable methodology to do so.

The Sarasvati and the Aryans form currently the headlines of the politics of the archaeology of the Indus Civilization. What is surprising is that there is a host of highly respectable scholars—R.P. Chanda, M.S. Vats, P. Kane, B.N. Dutta and others—who had no problem about postulating an interaction or even a phase of co-existence between this civilization and the writers of the Vedas. I have pointed out the significance of their writings in some detail in *The Battle for Ancient India*. A major historical question is why any suggestion of the association of the Indus Civilization with the people behind the Vedas is taken these days as the handiwork of Indian traditionalists or Hindu fundamentalists. I am not in a position to answer this question, but I would say that the attempt of R.S. Bisht to interpret Dholavira town-planning in terms of his citations of the *Rigveda* seems to make clear sense. It seems to be generally ignored that M.S. Vats, the major excavator of Harappa, interpreted the themes of the Cemetery H ware paintings in terms of the Vedic rituals related to the disposal of the dead. If I understand him clearly, Dharamveer Sharma, the excavator of Sinauli, finds some significant correspondence between these burials of the Harappan tradition and some later Vedic descriptions of the disposal of the dead.

Behind the headline themes, however, lies an extensive ground of disputed territory which covers virtually every detailed aspect of this civilization—distribution, chronology, the basic archaeological trajectory, trade, sculpture, continuity, religion, etc. The first thing to remember about distribution is that the Harappan pottery painting tradition continues right up to the Siwaliks, whether in Panjab, Haryana or western Uttar Pradesh. To anybody who has covered the ground here, it is overwhelmingly obvious that this is a vast area and offers no easy explanation of Harappan cultural growth here. It would be wrong to envisage the archaeology of this phase in this region merely as a case of Harappan expansion from the west to the east. Besides, there is a clear and uninterrupted case of continuity from the Harappans to the early historic period here. There is no break between the Harappans and the Painted Grey Ware at Alamgirpur in R.N. Singh's excavations. Interestingly, there was no break even in Y.D. Sharma's excavations. He interpreted what he found as a break. Incidentally, this points to the close impact of this civilization on what was happening in at least the upper Ganga Plain. This is something which has also been suggested by the association of the Copper Hoards with the Harappans at Sinauli.

If, however, you open the books which are widely followed in the Indian universities on Indus studies and written by American scholars like G. Possehl and M. Kenoyer, you will find that the Indus Civilization was the result of an interaction between cultures extending well into the Middle East and Central Asia and that there was single trajectory of its development with the growth of wheat-barley agriculture at Mehrgarh at its head. They try to minimise the tradition of rice or millet agriculture as parallel trajectories of development. In Gujarat, they and their Indian associates cannot look beyond the civilization's West Asiatic trade, forgetting that the Gujarat area has always been the centre of India's external trade across the Indian ocean. Just as not everything in pre-industrial Gujarat was controlled by its maritime trade, all the Indus settlements that we have in this region could not have come into existence in response to this trade. The basic politics of the Indus civilizational studies is eventually simple. To persons like the present writer, the Indus Civilization lies at the head of the Indian High Tradition, the tradition embodied at the highest level of Indian thought, because of the intricacy of its various continuities and links with the later proto-historic and historic India. To many others, mostly Western scholars, the Indus Civilization is rooted in the middle Asian interaction sphere and even the roots of the famous so-called priest-king image have to be sought in the art tradition of West Asia. Rita Wright, the author of a recent book on the Indus Civilization published by the Cambridge University Press, does not even bother to seriously raise the issue of Indus continuity, nor does she think it worthwhile to discuss the salient points raised in this context by various Indian scholars. I am not surprised by this because, as in Western Indology, in archaeology also Western scholars write essentially for their fellow Western scholars.

It is my professional and personal experience that a large section of the current First World Archaeology is plainly colour-conscious—racist, if you like—in relation to the archaeology of the Third World as practised by the Third World scholars themselves. An intriguing issue has emerged regarding the beginning of iron metallurgy in India. The dates from Malhar clearly indicate that there was even iron ploughshare in this area near Banaras around 1800 BC. The dates of this level from other related sites such as Raja Nala Ka Tila and Dadupur also underline the antiquity of iron in the agriculture of the central Ganga Plain being considerably earlier than 1000 BC. In his review of *The Battle for Ancient India* in the January-March 2009 issue of *Journal of the American Oriental Society*, G. Possehl criticizes me in the following terms:

"Chakrabarti positions India as the possible epicenter for the beginnings of iron technology. He holds that the art of smelting iron began in ancient India and spread from there to other parts of Europe and Asia. It has been reasonably clear for a number of years that the widespread use of iron begins at about 1000 BC (possibly a century or so earlier) in the broad belt from the Mediterranean to the South China Sea."

This is interesting in the sense that I consider India to be only one of the early centres of iron metallurgy (not as *the possible epicentre*). Secondly, nowhere have I written that iron technology went from India to 'other parts of Europe and Asia'. Thirdly, to say, as Possehl does, that the widespread use of iron began only about 1000 BC or 'possibly a century or so earlier' is a travesty of truth in the light of the radiocarbon dates from Malhar and other related sites. Possehl is certainly not above lying about what somebody has or has not written.

By now, it should be clear enough that the study of ancient India is a vast field of various conflicting ideas, all with political implications. *The more closely we look at it and examine its various premises, the better we shall understand the web of interests and counterinterests behind the ideas related to our past. However, the basic task of distilling a people's history of India out of the archaeological sources must go on and be set up as the primary yardstick to judge all nebulous and conflicting theories.*

REFERENCES

Chakrabarti, Dilip K. and Sukhdev Saini. 2009. *The Problem of the Sarasvati River and Notes on the Archaeological Geography of Haryana and Indian Panjab*. Delhi: Aryan Books.

Chakrabarti, Dilip K. 1976. India and the Druids. *Antiquity* 50(197): 66-67.

——. 1997. *Colonial Indology: Sociopolitics of the Ancient Indian Past.* Delhi: Munshiram Manoharlal.

——. 2006. *The Oxford Companion to Indian Archaeology*. Delhi: OUP.

——. 2008. *The Battle for Ancient India.* Delhi: Aryan Books.

——. 2009a. *Globalization and Indian Archaeology, and Other Essays.* Banaras: Department of Ancient Indian History, Culture and Archaeology, Banaras Hindu University.

——. 2009b. Who Owns the Indian Past ? The Case of the Indus Civilization. Delhi: India International Centre, Occasional Publications 11.

Danino, M. 2010. *The Lost River: The Trail of the Sarasvati.* Delhi: Penguin.

Franklin, M. 1997. Power to the People; Socio-politics and the Archaeology of Black Americans. *Historical Archaeology* 31(3): 36-50.

Gero, J.M., D.M. Laacy and M. Blakey (eds.). 1983. *The Socio-Politics of Archaeology*. Department of Anthropology, University of Massachusetts at Amherst.

Habib, I. 2001. Imaging River Sarasvati: A Defence of Commonsense. *Social Scientist* 29: 46-74.

Hock, H.H. 2000. Whose Past Is It? Linguistic Pre- and Early History and Self-Identification in Modern South Asia. *Studies in the Linguistic Sciences* 30(2): 51-74.

Lal, B.B. 2005. *The Homeland of the Aryans: Evidence of Rigvedic Flora, Fauna and Archaeology*. Delhi: Aryan Books.

Rajan, K., V.P. Yathees Kumar and S. Selvakumar. 2009. *Catalogue of Archaeological Sites in Tamil Nadu*. 2 vols. Thanjavur: Heritage India Trust.

Thomas, E. 1883. The Rivers of the Vedas, and How the Aryans Entered India. *JRAS*, pp. 357-86.

Yadava, M.G., K.S. Saraswat, I.B. Singh and R. Ramesh. 2007. Evidences of Early Human Occupation in the Limestone Caves of Bastar. *Current Science* 93(6): 820-23.

5

The Study of Ancient India

Some Historical and National Considerations

The ancient past of India came in for modern scrutiny in the middle of the eighteenth century. There were Graeco-Roman references to some ancient Indian cities and other geographical features, and the most important preliminary concern was to identify some of them in terms of modern Indian geography. For instance, what was the location of Pataliputra, a city for which the Greek Megasthenes left behind an elaborate description? It was identified with Patna in the late eighteenth century by the English geographer James Rennell.

In the field of working out the basic ancient historical frame of India, an important initial step was taken by William Jones who identified Sandrokottos of the Greek sources with Chandragupta Maurya, and as the date of Sandrokottos was known to be in the late 4th century BC from his association in the Greek context, the date of Chandragupta also fell in place.

With these two starting points the study of ancient India took off. However, what was the intellectual context in which it took off? The first concern was to relate India to the scheme of world history as it was then understood. It has to be noted that before Darwin published his ideas in the mid-nineteenth century, this scheme of world history had to be the Biblical scheme. If one accepts this scheme of the world being created by God on a particular date, one also has to accept that all human beings and civilizations were related in origin to one of the three sons of Noah—Ham, Sem and Japhet. William Jones emphasized this point in various ways, including his championing of the belief that Sanskrit, Greek and Latin were linguistically related. This was hardly a novel matter because, having descended from the God's world, all ancient languages had at some point to be related. In fact, in one of his early discourses, Jones put Sanskrit at par not merely with Greek and Latin but also with Peruvian and Japanese. It is indeed curious that only the Greek and Latin bit are now remembered.

The second intellectual context is no less interesting. The eighteenth century was the age of Enlightenment in Europe, especially France. This was an age when there was a conscious movement to break away from the Judaic and Christian orthodoxy and seek the origins of culture and civilization outside it. Initially China was the most favoured area from this point of view, but soon India came into the picture. Some people, including Voltaire believed that India and/or Central Asia was the centre from which civilization got disseminated elsewhere. Some interesting writings, all championing the cause of India as the centre of culture and civilization and invoking migrations of learned Brahmins and Buddhists to areas as far west as Scotland,were published in the first half of the nineteenth century and the last part of the eighteenth. One may note that all the writings of the Asiatic Society scholars glorifying Sanskrit and its literature belong to this period when there was no intellectual compulsion to view ancient India and its language and institutions in derogatory ways.

However, the idea that India could be an original centre of culture and civilization, as the Encyclopaedists thought or the people trying to relate India to the Biblical scheme of the world thought, came to an end around the middle of the nineteenth century. In fact, the end of this idea tallies well with the date of the revolution of 1857. This is one of the clear proofs in the Indian context that academic ideas in the humanities and social sciences at least are intimately related to the contemporary power structure.

The second half of the nineteenth century witnessed a number of interrelated things in the field of ancient India. There was steady progress in the understanding of the ancient literary sources and the associated dynastic chronology, partly on the basis of the English translations of the accounts of the Chinese pilgrims Zuangzang and Faxian and also on the basis of the translations of the Sinhalese texts of *Mahavamsa* and *Dipavamsa*. It was also during this period that Cunningham undertook his archaeological surveys, mapping out the historical potential of various sites throughout the country.

Secondly, different linguistic hypotheses gained ground during this period, the Aryan concept being the most important of them. The concept gained respectability in the voluminous writings of F. Max Müller, a German Sanskritist who never visited India and whose opinion of anything Indian except spirituality was very low. The point is that Max Müller was widely read by Indians, and the idea that the rulers of India of the period, the British, and the higher classes among the subject people of India belonged to the same racial stock had great appeal to many Indians, especially those of the upper order. The urgency with which even people like R.C. Dutt (1848–1909) accepted this idea and described the age of the establishment of the Aryan rule in India as among its most glorious periods must have sounded fairly distressing to those outside the Aryan pale. In fact, this is precisely what happened. Reaction had been sharp from the Dravidian Tamil Nadu, social reformer Jyotiba Phule (1827–1890) and constitutional expert and social reformer B.R. Ambedkar (1891–1956). A few comments may perhaps be made here on Dutt. One of the earliest members of the Indian Civil Service, Dutt was a nationalist, theorising about the drain of wealth from India. He also wrote two inspiring novels in Bengali with clear nationalist undertones, *Maharashtra Jiban Prabhat* and *Rajput Jiban Sandhya*. He also translated the *Rigveda* into Bengali. However, he could not go against the established scholarship of the time and had no difficulty in accepting the Aryan hypothesis. The inability or refusal to question the basic structure of the study of ancient India has possibly been the weakest point of the nationalist Indian scholarship.

Thirdly, hard racist ideas had come to rule academia in the name of science by the middle of the nineteenth century. The correlation in timing between the development of comparative philology or historical linguistics, as it is called nowadays, and the consolidation of racist ideas is striking. J.F. Blumenbach who first divided human groups into a few racial types wrote towards the end of the eighteenth century and so did William Jones, the so-called father of comparative philological studies. The racial classification of India took concrete shape with the publication of Risley's scheme in the census operation of 1901. It is indeed interesting to point out that the complete acceptance of the idea of Aryan invasion of India and the associated language schemes and the first major publication of the racial scheme of India took place in about the same period, thus highlighting the close relationship between the postulated language history and racial history of the country. In the case of India further consolidation of this approach took place in the 1931 census when J.H. Hutton, later professor of Social Anthropology in Cambridge, and B.S. Guha, later Director of the Anthropological Survey of India amplified the earlier scheme of Risley. These racial schemes of Indian culture and history were accepted without a question by scholars like S.K. Chatterji and others in the first volume of the series on the history and culture of the Indian people. Once again it highlights our premise that even our nationalist scholars and historians could not challenge some of the fundamental speculations about the ancient Indian studies.

Before turning to the story of further developments, one has to point out that the Aryan language concept went hand in hand with the concept of race, and the reason of its persistent strength even today is closely linked with the Western scholars' quest to discover a past world situation in which the supremacy of the Western powers and their language in the world stage would be adequately reflected in the ancient context. If we are asked why many non-Western scholars are also equally interested in keeping alive the myth of a pristine Aryan language and its dissemination, the answer is that it can be found in the socio-politics of the historical studies of the countries these non-Western scholars are from. I shall come back to this problem in the context of the Indian scholarship later.

There were two important developments in the field of ancient Indian studies: the discovery of the text of *Arthasastra* in 1905, (the editing of the text by Shamasastry in 1909, and the publication of Shamasastry's English translation of the text in 1915) and discovery of the Indus Civilization in the

1920s. The publication of the text of Kautilya's 'Arthasastra' may be less momentous than the discovery of the Indus Civilization, but it was very significant in its own right. It showed at a stroke that there was an organized study of the various aspects of statecraft in ancient India and the fact that it belonged by and large to the Mauryan times also showed that the development of the first pan-Indian state was associated with developed and organized ideas of administration. Further, ancient India was not concerned solely with matters of mind but also with many mundane matters including espionage and warfare. The date of the *Arthasastra* has been discussed many times but without specific results, but on the whole, the overall image of a highly centralized administration keeping all spheres of life under its supervision is likely to tally more with the powerful and pan-Indian Mauryan state than with any later development.

The discovery of the Indus Civilization caught the scholars of ancient India completely unawares. The only thing which excited them was whether it was Vedic or post-Vedic. S.K. Chatterji in 1924 expressed his belief, for no particular reason, that the people of this civilization were likely to have spoken a language belonging to the Dravidian family. The alacrity with which this opinion, although based on nothing profound or verifiable, was accepted in Tamil Nadu is well known. The publication in 1931 of Marshall's three-volume report on the Mohenjo-daro excavations was a very important event because that brought out the true outline of the different aspects of the life at Mohenjo-daro, including religion, and sharply emphasized his belief that the civilization was deeply rooted in the Indian soil. If Marshall believed that the civilization was post and non-

Vedic, there were scholars who believed that many Vedic elements could be seen in this civilization.

On the whole, this is where the study of ancient India stood in 1947. By this time it had about two hundred years of research in the background: ancient places identified and archaeological sites mapped; the ancient texts translated into English and examined for their historical contents; the laying down of the basic frameworks of ancient Indian dynastic and other aspects of history; and finally, the discovery of the Indus Civilization and its Indian roots. The Aryan and other associated linguistic ideas were accepted as facts along with the theoretical premise of race-language-culture correlation. Expression of Indian nationalism did not find expression in anything more serious than the idea of republican institutions in ancient India. There were also perfectly logical attempts to put back the dates of some texts by one or two centuries and deny that the Greeks, Romans and other external forces had exerted particularly powerful influences on different technological and cultural aspects of India's ancient development.

The post-Independence study of ancient India may best be seen in its initial phase in the relevant volumes of the *History and Culture of the Indian People* series. Its first volume, *The Vedic Age*, was a summary of the generally accepted scholarly ideas about these texts and the Aryan hypothesis, and there was also an analysis of the essential picture of the traditional and legendary view of the first phase of Indian political history. From the second volume onward, there was a routine synthesis of what was known of the various phases of ancient India. With some of this analysis one could disagree on technical grounds but such matters of disputes had long been known, and nowhere in the text of these volumes can one find any unnecessary glorification of ancient India.

Soon after Independence, any expression of nationalism in writings on ancient India came under attack from historians who later on became institutionally powerful. For instance, in 1959, in the first edition of his book *Aspects of Political Ideas and Institutions in Ancient India,* R.S. Sharma dwelt at length on the historiography of ancient Indian state. When he considers the merits and limitations of ' the nationalist and revivalist approach' to the study of the past Indian polity, one wonders why it has to be called 'revivalist' simply because most of the historians who wrote on ancient Indian political institutions were writing in the context of the nationalist movement and made clear comments on the merits of these institutions. Among the further limitations of this approach he states that by their fulsome adoration of ancient Hindu institutions, they tended to antagonise the Muslims, although it was not done deliberately. Sharma has not cited any detailed Muslim response here. The whole thing is possibly a concoction on his part because why should any community take umbrage if a different community's institutions long before its own time in the land are praised. In short, Sharma calls the nationalist historians 'revivalist' and then calls them responsible for giving fuel to Hindu-Muslim sense of separation and jealousy.

By the time Romila Thapar wrote an article on interpretations in ancient Indian history in *History and Theory* in 1968, the tone of criticism became more strident. In Thapar's language, "nationalism was replaced by a form of militant Hinduism and earlier attempts at proving the indigenous origin of all things Indian were accentuated". If Sharma and Thapar had undertaken detailed research showing that the professional historians of ancient India were all communalists and believers in militant Hinduism, we would have had the opportunity of critically analysing the data cited by them. As they have not done so, we cannot give a moment's credence to them. In their professional writings our nationalist historians are not known to have wilfully distorted data. On the other hand, I find Thapar's opinion that "earlier attempts at proving the indigenous origin of all things Indian were accentuated" a wilful distortion of truth. Which nationalist history did Thapar have in mind? As far as I know, the professional study of ancient Indian history and archaeology had been out and out diffusionist till recently. Not long after Thapar wrote, H.D. Sankalia of the Deccan College wrote that for India the sun of culture and civilization always rose in the West. His was not a lone opinion of the period. Such opinions are still voiced by many scholars both inside and outside the Deccan College. My contention is that Sharma, Thapar and people who belonged to their group wanted to justify their own position by raising the bogey of communalism and militant Hinduism among the professional historians before them.

I have another contention. Declaring India from time to time as an ageless colony of foreign powers has been a pastime of our ancient historians and archaeologists. Why the voice of our 'historical materialists' was never raised against it? Which principle of 'historical materialism' says that the cultural development anywhere has to be conditioned primarily by foreign influences? In which national area of archaeological scholarship does the find of three copper arrowheads make you undertake almost a global journey in search of their parallels and origin? (V.N. Misra undertook such a journey in order to 'locate' three copper arrowheads from Bagor). Post-Independence ancient Indian historical scholarship of the professional variety is not known to believe in nationalism. If a few people before Independence tried to show that there were a few good things in ancient India including their political institutions, we should respect them, instead of calling them 'militant Hindus' or 'Hindu revivalists'.

In the book which we have cited earlier, Sharma called himself a 'historical materialist', drawing on *Ancient Society* by Henry Morgan and *The Origin of the Family, Private Property and the State* by Friedrich Engels for ideas. The problem does not lie in what you believe in. The problem lies in how you try to build up your case and how logical you are in putting forward your structure. It is time Sharma's, Thapar's and their fellow travellers' writings are critically analysed in detail from the point of view of logical academic arguments and grip of the primary data.

In any case, the tendency we have seen in Sharma's or Thapar's writings soon led to the political creation of the Indian Council of Historical Research in the early 1970s. It is not for me to go into the roots or justification of setting up this government-sponsored institution, but I believe that the total concentration of power to fund historical research in the country in a single government-sponsored organization which in turn has been controlled by government-nominated members of specific political orientations has led to unprecedented politicisation and consequent criminalisation of this field since the early 1970s, irrespective of the parties the historian politicians in control owe their allegiance to. I am aware that virtually anybody retired in the Indian historical academia could manage to secure for himself a fellowship to do research. In most cases, no research in the form of major publications was done by these retired academics. As long as one was of a right political hue and had friends in the organization's administrative set-up, there was no problem in getting money from it. I gather that Arun Shourie has discussed some of these aspects in *Eminent Historians* (1998), but the rot is limited not merely to the 'eminent ones'; it is far more widespread than that.

What are the major grounds of dispute in the study of ancient India today? The first of these disputes is about the continuity of the Indian civilization and Hinduism, and it is more visible in archaeological studies than in the more traditional literary fields. It is in archaeology that the problem has sharply emerged in recent years and it has also got a lot to do with the problem of religion of the Indus civilization. To many early scholars including the editor of the first report on Mohenjo-daro, there are unmistakable shadows of later day Hinduism in what has been excavated at that site: the Yogic practice, Siva-Pasupati cult, representation of *Saptamatrika*, sacredness of *Pipul* tree, ritualistic character of mother goddess figurines, ritual use of water, and so on. The presence of Siva has been categorically demonstrated by the find of a terracotta *Sivalinga* set in a *Yonipatta* in the Mature Harappan level of Kalibangan. I am not suggesting for a moment that Hinduism in all its varieties and complexities as we find it today was present in the Indus Civilization because modern Hinduism also is as much a product of historical evolution as any other religion or cultural phenomenon. All that we are suggesting is that many traits of later-day Hinduism can be traced back to the Indus Civilization. In fact, the continuity of a mother goddess worship tradition has been traced back to *c.* 9000 BC in a Stone Age context in Madhya Pradesh.

However, the continuity of Hinduism or Hindu ritualistic beliefs is something which is unacceptable to a significant number of scholars. How many books on ancient India emphasize this aspect of continuity?

One of the reasons why this is so is due to our ingrained belief in the theory of Aryan migration and the consequent belief in the origin of Hinduism in the Vedas. All that I would say is that the linguistic premise of a common Aryan language or a common Aryan homeland may all be true but strictly in the context of historical language studies alone. Like all linguistic premises of this kind, this is unverifiable and cannot be dated in its own term. This has got nothing to do with archaeology or history. Whether there is archaeological continuity from the Indus Civilization onward can be debated and discussed, but there is no scope for debate regarding the archaeological or historical presence of any particular group of people called the Aryans. The Vedas no doubt exist, but they exist as a category of Indian literature without the vast Indo-European constructs behind it. The sooner we get used to the idea of a history of ancient India without the Aryans or any other linguistically constructed category such as the Dravidians, Austrics, etc. the better. I am not one of those who fall over backward at the name of 'multi-disciplinary research'. You do research in your own field and take the help of other disciplines as far as they help you realize your own research goals. You do not take the help of any approach which makes you flounder helplessly in mud, which is exactly what the so-called historical linguistics does to archaeology. From the Indian national point of view, belief in fanciful linguistic reconstructs can be very damaging because in the long run they plant the seed of implacable differences in identity between different language-speaking groups. Rajiv Malhotra and Aravindan Neelakandan highlight some of these dangers in their *Breaking India*. The dangers are very real, as ethnic strifes, based precisely on imagined differences in the concerned groups' historical trajectories, in many parts of the world, show.

What I fail to understand is why ancient historians like Sharma and Thapar have always been ardent believers in the Aryan idea. It is possible that the idea of continuity of Hinduism is anathema to them. To them, there does not seem to be much difference between belief in this idea and Hindu fundamentalism.

How is it that a large percentage of foreign archaeologists working in India are believers in the Aryan hypothesis? The only explanation is that they like to view the Indian past as a disjointed series of interactions with different people. Further, the idea of the coming of the Aryans satisfies their notion of a superior group of people taking over India. On the national level, India has every reason to be wary of foreign archaeological presence because of many of their ideas can plant seeds of difference among Indians regarding their identities. The leader of a particular foreign archaeological group interested in working on the Indus Civilization did not hesitate to poke fun, in print, at Hindu deity Hanuman and also make unsupportable statements about Hindu religion. Recently, another member of this group has published a general study of the Indus Civilization without even raising the issue of the massive continuity of this civilization. The type of attitude which I see here among these archaeologists, J.M. Kenoyer and Rita Wright, has been discussed well in *Invading the Sacred, an Analysis of Hinduism Studies in America* (2007, eds. K. Ramaswamy, A. Nicholas and A. Banerjee).

I may also point out that the study of ancient India suffers from two serious limitations in modern India. First, it is marginalised in the Indian university framework. The main emphasis of most of our History departments is modern India, the history of the last two hundred years. In fact, professional

Indian historians are interested generally in the twentieth century and later India. In Delhi University, for instance, ancient India is taught in the first year honours, and by the time the students come up to their MA and are supposed to select their MA options, they have forgotten what they studied about ancient India in their first year. Most of them opt for 'modern India'. The second danger lies in the fact that in the Indian academia, the difference between those who have been taught in the English medium and those who have been taught in the medium of vernacular languages is huge. It is incredible, but the fact remains that it is the vernacular medium students whose roots are deep in the soil. It is they who can read vernacular literature in original. It is they who are in a position to raise original questions about the ancient history of the land. As far as my experience goes, the furthest the English medium students of History and their teachers can go is to faithfully show their familiarity with the currently fashionable academic theories. There may be exceptions, but they are rather rare. The danger lies in the fact that the vernacular medium students are almost invariably neglected in the teaching frames and very few of them prefer to do research later on. This is one of the reasons why research rooted in the land is hard to come by in ancient India.

Apart from the socio-political factors I have pointed out, the study of ancient India has a few inherent limitations of its own. The main thing is the paucity of sources, and K.A.N. Sastri, in his famous study of the Cholas, wrote of "the utter impossibility of basing any part of the ancient history of India solely, or even primarily, upon literary evidence".

There is no way we can get out of these and other limitations. Whichever sociology we may swear by, that will not illuminate our ancient historical scene. Archaeology has enormously helped in expanding the character of ancient historical sources but let us remember that about 85% of the excavations conducted since Independence have remained unpublished and that while advertising for the Director General of the Archaeological Survey of India sometime back, the Ministry of Culture of the Government of India found it completely unnecessary to emphasize that they needed an archaeologist, first and foremost, and a good one at that. According to the relevant advertisement, (F. No-4-36/2009/ASI), the only firm requirement was that the aspiring candidates had served three years on a specified senior salary-scale. Otherwise, the net thrown was very wide: a post-graduate qualification (subject unspecified and no emphasis on the applicant's basic academic performance) and 15 years' experience in any of the following subjects: Archaeology, Architecture, Conservation, History, and Anthropology. Further, there had to be five years' experience (out of the specified fifteen years) in 'administration matters'. A bachelor's degree of Management was considered desirable. Apparently, the Ministry was not looking exclusively for a field- archaeologist of proven brilliance to run its Archaeological Survey which, incidentally, is possibly the largest organisation of its kind in the world. One does not have to be surprised by this because according to the concerned ministry's own website, the Archaeological Survey of India is no more than a maintenance organization on the model of PWD.

On a different level, let me point out that the study of inscriptions had always been one of the basic strengths of the Archaeological Survey. Today, a visit to the headquarter of this 'branch' in Mysore is likely to be distressing because of the lack of morale among the Survey epigraphers, if not for anything else. The study of epigraphy and palaeography has to be raised to a higher level in the universities too. The Survey's conservation policy needs a close re-examination. I do not understand how the Ajanta paintings have been allowed to lose the warmth of their colours and how paintings at Sittanavasal have been allowed to be completely obliterated in one lifetime. I also do not understand why wholesale reconstructions are the rule of the day at conserved sites, basically changing their ancient character and ambience. It is indeed saddening that there is such a vast gap between the ideal and the reality in Indian archaeology.

However, behind all this litany of sorrow still lies the basic task of researching ancient India. About two hundred years of research has built tapestries of various kinds in this field. One major tapestry is missing, and that is history in relation to the present landscape of the country. People were moving about in the ancient context as they do now. They carved out kingdoms, cities and villages; they prospected and mined for resources, conducted trade and battles; they crossed rivers, passed through jungles, high mountain passes and deserts. How do they all relate to the land that we see, the land which still survives? If all these different aspects of studies can be translated in terms of the actual grounds which we can identify, the ancient history of the country is likely to be far more meaningful to us than it is now. I have attempted to achieve some of this in my own way, and my experience is that the ground that the ancients trod is still there before us. We know that Asoka visited Lumbini, the birthplace of the Buddha, but assuming that he travelled to Lumbini from his capital Pataliputra, can we check his footsteps today, more than two thousand years later? Can we know where he was likely to have crossed the Ganga, having set out from Pataliputra for Lumbini early one morning? Where could he spend that night and where could he have crossed the Ghaghra? It is certainly possible to know all these things, provided you care for this kind of history—history that takes you to the dust of this ancient land. In England, the study of this kind of topographical history goes back to the 17th century, providing a very important touch of reality to the historical knowledge of the country. It is still a neglected field in India but is likely to lead to a fresh understanding between us and this land. We would also realize that what happened in the ancient past has still not gone out of the landscape.

Finally, I would say that the relationship between ancient Indian studies and the modern socio-politics related to India as a country is more important than we realize. Many of our old premises regarding ancient India are academically wrong—its race-language-culture framework, the way its sources have been looked at, the ideas related to the origin of its various cultural elements, the way the different sections of the country have interacted, etc. Each of these has a bearing on how we think of our country as an ancient land and each of these is in need of careful scrutiny. It is unlikely that the established framework of these studies, as sanctioned by the dominant power among the Indian and foreign academia, will yield its place to the onrush of new thoughts and approaches quietly or peacefully. If a very senior Indian archaeologist can write that for India, the sun of culture and civilization always rose in the West and if challenging opinions such as these is considered an act of fundamentalism by some of the country's establishment historians, we must realize that we are in for sharp battles. Such battles can be fought only by well-trained, nationally committed historians and archaeologists. Filling the web with nebulous ideas is no answer.

6

Power, Politics and *Ariya Mayai* ('Aryan Illusion') in the Study of Indian History

THE CONTEXT

While approaching the Indian side of the display in the British Museum's Asian gallery, one comes across a stone sculpture of Surya, and the museum's explanatory note, as observed on September 21, 2008, had the following introductory statement:

> The sacred traditions brought into India by the Aryans were eventually written down in texts known as the Vedas. The best known of these is the Rigveda, dated to about 1200 BC.

The museum scholars who penned the above sentence were almost certainly unaware of the socio-political implication of their premise, but it may nonetheless be interesting to spell it out: Hinduism developed out of the belief-system brought in by the Indo-Aryans to India about 1200 BC. The underlying implication is that Hinduism is not something which can be considered an inherent product of the Indian soil. It was something which was associated with a group of migrants and, thus, by implication, as much indigenous to the land as Islam and Christianity which came many centuries later. Secondly, the premise ignores the continuity of the basic column of Indian culture and tradition, supposing a major break around 1200 BC.

The scholars who wrote the explanatory note on this British Museum Surya figure are by no means isolated, even in 2008, in their opinion. Upinder Singh, a Delhi University history professor and the author of a book on ancient India (2008), poses, quite early in her volume *A History of Ancient and Early Mediaeval India*, the question "who were the Indo-Aryans" without casting even a shadow of doubt on the assumption that they were actual people and had a specific homeland. If one considers this, along with her tacit acceptance of the opinion that the earliest Indo-Aryan text dated from *c.* 1200–1000 BC or 1500–1000 BC and her apprehension in viewing the Harappan religious beliefs 'through the lens of later-day Hinduism', one realizes that this Delhi University professor and the British Museum scholars whose opinion has been cited above share the same attitude to the Indian past, i.e. Hinduism is as much indigenous to the Indian land as any other religious beliefs brought in by later immigrants.

Scholars like Upinder Singh are silent about a crucial issue: if the Harappan religious beliefs should not be viewed through the lens of later-day Hinduism, with which lens should it be viewed? After all, this is the lens through which the first major report on the Indus Civilization tried to make sense of its religious beliefs. They should also be aware that the attempt to relegate Hinduism to the status of just another 'immigrant' religion in the subcontinental context has a long history and different modern manifestations, including the one which denies Hinduism the privilege of being a single religion and ascribes its current status as the majority religion of India to the decision of the British census operators not to classify people according to their Saivite, Vaishnavite and myriad other affiliations. The latter opinion has been expressed by many Western Indologists. The Hindus preferred to call their religion Sanatana Dharma, a term which occurs in a Sanskrit inscription of *c.* 6th century AD.

The historical trajectory of the Indo-European linguistics is not my concern, nor am I competent to speak about it. I shall, however, draw attention to the facts that the Aryan concept emerged in the 18th century when the Biblical theory of creation was in vogue, and that the emergence of this concept coincided with the emergence of the concept of race in European thought. It will be interesting to point out how these two concepts went hand in hand and provided the philosophical backdrop of viewing the human civilization in terms of discrete categories of language and their correlation with a superior/inferior hierarchy of race—a view which also fitted eminently in the framework of European or a 'superior' group of people's expansion and dominance all over the globe. In Archaeology, I shall enquire when did it become commonplace to integrate the language and race framework into archaeological thinking, and how it is doing now. In certain quarters of modern archaeology, the precepts of comparative philology have acquired great charm and attempts are afoot to view a wide array of things from Neolithic beginnings to contacts across the Indian Ocean in terms of the speculations derived from comparative philology.

THE NOTION OF 'ARYAN ILLUSION' IN TAMIL NADU

The title of a book published in Tamil in 1943 by C.N. Annadurai who later became the first non-Congress chief minister of Tamil Nadu, was *Ariya Mayai* or 'Aryan Illusion' He wrote that there was no concrete evidence to prove that the Aryans invaded India and destroyed the Dravidians: "*Our people will be liberated from ignorance only on the day we are freed from the Aryan illusion.*" (Barnett 1976: 73)

If one believes, as I do, that there is no conceivable logical way to correlate a pre- or non-literate archaeological culture with a particular language or language family, one has to wonder why the Aryan concept, which does precisely that, has persisted for more than 200 years. The only way of justifying such an exercise is to accept the framework of an admittedly imaginary language history that has been constructed for the concerned geographical area by comparative philologists or historical linguists. The question which is seldom asked is why should archaeologists or, for that matter, anybody else except comparative philologists, accept the untestable premises of prehistoric language history? Can 'comparative philology' date specific events in language history or can it offer any proof that its reconstruction of prehistoric language dispersals approximates even a modicum of historical reality? If 'comparative philology' is incapable of doing any of these things, what does archaeology gain by attaching itself to it? I shall try to answer this question by drawing attention to some India-related examples.

There is an archaeological school which links the beginning of rice cultivation in East, Southeast, and by implication, South Asia to the spread of Austric language super-family comprising the Austronesian language family of Taiwan, the Malay archipelago, Pacific islands, and Madagascar, and the Austro-Asiatic language family of mainland Southeast Asia with extensions in east India (cf. Diamond and Bellwood 2003). However, in the case of rice cultivation in India, the earliest domesticated evidence is dated

7th-6th millennia BC and comes from the site of Lohuradeva near Gorakhpur (Tewari et al. 2004). This is a clear case of independent beginning of rice cultivation in the central Ganga Plain. In fact, multiple beginnings of rice have been advocated on the basis of genetical considerations as well (Londo et al. 2006), and apparently there is no reason to consider it linked to only one area in its possible geographical range or to associate it with any language dispersal. Coming to a more recent chronological horizon, one may refer to the handling of Indian archaeological data on the beginning of iron period in the mid-1960s when it was linked to the coming of the Indo-Aryan language speakers to India. Even on the basis of the same set of archaeological data it was possible to argue in the mid-1970s that the beginning of iron technology in India was an early and independent process (Chakrabarti 1976b). This premise was substantiated in the 1990s by a wide range of archaeological data from different parts of the country (Tewari 2003).

In 2007, David Anthony, an American professor of anthropology, published a book entitled *The Horse, the Wheel and Language: How Bronze-Age Riders from the Eurasian Steppes Shaped the Modern World.* India figures only marginally in this discussion, but the author's perception of the process which brought the Indo-European speakers to India is as follows.

Between *c.* 2000 BC and *c.* 1800 BC, two groups of archaeological cultures with their origins in the Ural region of Russia—the Petrovka and Alakul-Andronovo groups—settled in the Zeravshan River Valley of Tadjikistan and Uzbekistan and began mining for copper and tin. It was around this time that "horses and chariots appeared across the Near East, and the warfare of cities became dependent, for the first time, on welltrained horses". According to Anthony,

> the Old Indic Religion probably emerged among northern-inspired immigrants in the contact zone between the Zeravshan and Iran as a syncretic mixture of old central Asian and new Indo-European elements.
>
> *From this time forward the people of the Eurasian steppes remained directly connected with the civilization of central Asia, south Asia, and Iran, and through intermediaries, with China. The arid lands that occupied the centre of the Eurasian continent began to play a role in the transcontinental economics and politics* (Anthony 2007: 462).

The crucial chronological point of Indian contact of these horse/chariot-riding population of Central Asia is, as one reads above, the opening centuries of the second millennium BC. The *Rigveda*, according to Anthony, was composed between 1500 and 1300 BC. He makes no effort to enquire if horse and wheel could be known in India earlier. The earliest evidence of domesticated horse in the subcontinent is from the 5th millennium BC context at Rana Ghundai in the Zhob-Loralai area of northeast Baluchistan. The veterinary officer of the Loralai Cantonment, to whom the animal teeth discovered at the site were given for examination, found them "practically indistinguishable either in structure and size from those of our cavalry horses". Among the faunal remains of the Mature Indus Civilization levels at Harappa, Lothal, Surkotada and Kalibangan, horse-bones have been identified by a number of scholars including one from the Zoological Survey of India (for a summary, Lal 2002). The objections raised against the validity of these identifications do not deserve any credence (cf. Meadow and Patel 1997). There is even a terracotta representation of horse from the Indus context at Lothal. Equally revealing is Anthony's silence about the presence of terracotta representations of spoked wheels in the mature Indus civilization levels of Rakhigarhi, Kalibangan, Banawali (for a summary, Lal 2002) and Bhirrana (Rao 2005-2006). There is no doubt that both spoked wheel and horse were known in India long before the chronology suggested for this by Anthony.

I find the sub-title of Anthony's book intriguing—"How Bronze-Age Riders from the Eurasian Steppes Shaped the Modern World". What is intriguing about it is the sheer antiquity of such notions about Central Asia. In 1858, R.L. Mitra, one of the first Indian antiquarians, wrote something very similar. Central Asia, according to him, was a region from where "in the darkness of a time far beyond the limits of history, peoples and races have come forth to take possession of the earth" (Mitra 1858). It is also common knowledge that this idea goes further back to the beginning of the 19th century when it can be found in the writings of the German Romantics such as J.G. Herder and F. Schlegel (for the details, Poliakov 1974).

There is a major difference in the way this idea was expressed in the beginning of the 19th century and around the middle of that century. In 1789, an English mathematician in India, Reuben Burrow (1789), thought that the position of Equator was once further north, bringing about a better climatic condition in Central Asia which was then inhabited by the Hindus and from there the Hindu religion 'probably spread over the whole earth'. This romantic notion of India as an area which sent out roving bands of ascetics as missionaries of civilization died out by the middle of the 19th century. As I wrote earlier, "with the Raj firmly established, it was the time to begin to visualize the history and cultural process of India as a series of invasions and foreign rules" (Chakrabarti 1976). As far as India is concerned, there is a clear echo of Britain's Indian empire's power and politics in both Mitra's and Anthony's image of chariot-driving and horse-riding groups coming out of Central Asia.

In fact, William Jones' classic assertion that Sanskrit had an immemorial affinity with Latin and Greek was also rooted in the ground reality of British control of the late 18th century Bengal and the politics of its expansion elsewhere in India. I have emphasized (Chakrabarti 1988) that Jones' writings on India were in response to the contemporary political and intellectual need to relate India to the pre-evolutionary structure of European knowledge of the world's history and civilization. His famous 'third anniversary discourse' of February 1786—famous because it contains the sentence about the immemorial affinity between Sanskrit, Greek and Latin—also declares Sanskrit's 'immemorial affinity' with a long list of languages including 'the Chinese, Japanese and Peruvians'. In the days when the Biblical theory of creation was in vogue, all human families were supposed to have descended from the sons of Noah and thus they had to be mutually related. Jones' aim was to trace such linkages in the case of India and thus make India understandable to the European scholarship of the day, which was necessary in view of the increasing European/British power in the region. It must be understood that for more than 150 years before Jones, there was a close European mercantile familiarity with India, which resulted in voluminous written material on the country. No grand theme runs through these writings. Jones' grand narrative, including the germination of the subsequently full-blown Aryan idea, came about in the changed political context of the late 18th century India.

WHEN DID THE ARYAN IDEA BECOME IMPORTANT IN THE STUDY OF INDIAN HISTORY?

M. Elphinstone's *The History of India*, published in 1841 and the first major textbook of Indian history, set no store by it. Elphinstone was aware of how the Indo-European language question was shaping up, but he wrote that "to say that it spread from a central point" was a "gratuitous assumption" (Elphinstone 1841: 97-98). A few years later, however, J.C. Marshman (1867) had no doubt that the upper caste Hindus belonged to the 'conquering race'. In 1869, a British Indian official, George Campbell (1869), thought that the people of the hills north of Panjab were "among the purest Aryans in the world". That the message got down to the level of ordinary educated Indians possibly had something to do with F. Max Müller's voluminous writings on what he called 'the science of language'. Although Max Müller did not hide in print his contempt for the Indians (for the details, Chakrabarti 1997), he was a well-known scholar among the Indians for his English translation of the *Rigveda* and the editorship of the 'Sacred Books of India' series.

Before we take up the ramifications of this idea in the historical writings of the subsequent periods, it may be important to emphasize that the Aryan concept has been, almost from its very beginning, nothing but a racist idea embroiled in the notion of a hierarchy of superior and inferior people. Max Müller's statement that there is nothing called an Aryan skull hides, in fact, his own ambivalence in this matter. As it has been pointed out before,

> What mattered most was not Max Müller's personal opinion in this regard but what most of his contemporaries thought and passed on to the succeeding

> periods. It was the idea of correlation between the diverse elements of race, language, history and culture which was dominant throughout and fully triumphed in the end. (Chakrabarti 1997).

The idea that the rulers and the higher echelon of the ruled in India belonged to the same group of people was eagerly accepted by both sides, and served the interest of the empire from that point of view. A remarkable book of this category was E.B. Havell's *The History of the Aryan Rule in India in 1918* (Havell 1918). His is a celebrated name in the history of Bengal art in the early part of the 20th century. The motivation to write this book came from his belief that in honouring "our Aryan forerunners in India we shall both honour ourselves and make the most direct and effective appeal to Indian loyalty". On the Indian side, the eagerness with which the historians from R.C. Dutt (1889-90) onwards have clung to the Aryan invasion idea makes sad reading. To Dutt, 'Hindu Aryans' came as conquerors; to K.M. Panikkar they were 'fair-skinned' having contempt for the dark-skinned. According to R.K. Mukherjee (1956), another influential historian, "the history of India is mainly that of the Aryans in India". The socio-politics of such writings lies in the fact that the Indian historians who almost invariably came from the upper strata of the Indian caste system never took the trouble of hiding their elation at being considered the successors of people who colonized and civilized the land (for the details of this paragraph, Chakrabarti 1997).

By the middle of the nineteenth century, the Aryans, apart from emerging as a historical and racial issue, had acquired some social and political dimensions as well. It appears that the first step in this regard was taken by Christian missionaries. We quote from Rosalind O'Hanlon (1985: 80-81):

> Missionary propaganda... attempted to undermine the legitimacy of traditional practices by showing that they were quite recent innovations, running counter to the ancient beliefs of the Vedic society. John Wilson's book *India: Three Thousand Years Ago*, published in 1858, set out to describe the origins of the Aryan people, their arrival in the subcontinent and their conflict with the indigenous tribes, the nature of their customs and religious beliefs.

A clear manifestation of the missionary angle in the English translation of many of the ancient Hindu texts was the publication of such volumes as John Muir's Original Sanskrit Texts on the *Origin and History of the People of India, Their Religion and Institutions* in three volumes in 1868–1871. The repeated emphasis was on the fact that in the light of the original early texts of the Hindus, it was self-evident that Hinduism was not a revealed religion but had undergone various stages of social, moral, religious and intellectual developments. "The ideas and beliefs which are exhibited in their oldest documents are not the same as those which we encounter in their later writings" (Muir 1872 reprint, Vol. 1, p. 1). Interestingly, this missionary view lies at the root of a long traditional association between Sanskrit and 'Divinity'/Religion faculties of some Western universities. Cambridge and Oxford are among these universities. We have noticed how in the institution of Boden professorship in Sanskrit in Oxford, the hope that this will help in facilitating the conversion of Indians to Christianity played a role. The same hope was expressed by J. Cowell, the first professorial appointee in Sanskrit in Cambridge in 1867.

J.G. PHULE AND DAYANANDA SARASVATI

Jyotirao Govindrao Phule, the famous 19th century social reformer of Maharashtra, turned the Aryan hypothesis on its head. His basic idea of this matter was clearly formulated in his book *Slavery* (in This Civilized British Government under the Cloak of Brahmanism) published in Marathi in 1873 It would be helpful to quote some extracts from this book:

> Recent researches have demonstrated beyond a shadow of doubt that the Brahmins are not the aborigines of India. At some remote period of antiquity, probably more than 3000 years ago, the Aryan progenitors of the present Brahmin Race descended upon the plains of Hindoo Koosh... They appear to have been a race imbued with very high notions of self, extremely cunning, arrogant and bigoted... The aborigines whom the Aryans subjugated or displaced appear to have been a hardy and brave people from the determined front which they offered to these interlopers... The cruelties which the early European settlers practiced on the American Indians in their first settlements in the New World had certainly their parallel in India in the advent of the Aryans and their subjugation of the aborigines. (Deshpande 2002: 22-29).

Phule goes on to add that the Brahminical mythology, code of laws, caste system and priest-craft were all geared to making the life of the Brahmins easy whereas the Sudras were treated with nothing but contempt.

In contrast, Swami Dayananda Saraswati in the 11th chapter of *Satyarth Prakash* (1875) asserts that the Aryans had been in Aryavarta (India) since 'the beginning of the world'. Aryavarta under the Aryans was imagined to be a golden land.

> All the knowledge that is extant in the world originated in Aryavarta (India). Thence it spread to Egypt, thence to Greece, thence to the whole continent of Europe, thence to America and other countries. (Bharadwaja 1927: 313).

The Puranic form of Hinduism was anathema to Dayananda. He systematically exploded the myth of the wonders of India. As J.T.F. Jordens (1978: 112) comments, despite his enthusiastic portrayal of the image of an Aryan Vedic India complete with fire-arms, his exposure of Hinduism was 'a savage one'.

Among the non-Aryanist Indian writers, only B.R. Ambedkar had a correct academic perception of the situation. In the chapter on "Shudras versus Aryans" in *Who Were the Shudras?*, he wrote in 1946:

> ...the theory is based on nothing but pleasing assumptions and the inferences based on such assumptions. In the second place, the theory is a perversion of scientific investigation. It is not allowed to evolve out of facts. On the contrary the theory is pre-conceived and facts are selected to prove it. (Ambedkar 1970 reprint: 73-74).

In Tamil Nadu, the Aryan theory was at the heart of its non-Brahmin political tradition. There it took two forms. In one case, the Dravidians were thought to have contributed significantly to the Indian civilization, especially in its pre-Aryan form, and it was assumed that the later-day Indian civilization was the result of a synthesis between the Aryans and the Dravidians. G. Slater in his *The Dravidian Element in Indian Culture* (Slater 1924) rightfully diagnosed that, for an Indian, to be regarded as a Dravidian rather than an Aryan carried the sense of a denial of his 'kinship with the western European' and relegation to an inferior category. This, according to him, was the main stumbling block against a proper understanding of Dravidian contribution to Indian culture. Although published in 1925, only one year after the formal announcement of the discovery of the Indus Civilization, T.R. Shesha Iyengar's book *Dravidian India* (Iyengar 1925) carried a detailed discussion on the possibility of its being a Dravidian civilization. *Some Contributions of South India to Indian Culture* (1923) was the title of S. Krishnaswami Aiyangar's book, but there he adopted an approach which had major impacts on the study of the Tamil past and also on Tamil politics.

> History begins for India with the coming of the Aryans into the country. It may be said with almost equal truth that the history of South India... begins with the coming of the Aryans into the south. In this particular context the term "Aryan" seems to stand for the Brahman (Aiyangar 1923).

The second form taken by the Aryan theory in Tamil Nadu was a serious reaction against this approach which was synonymous with the maintenance of the Brahmanical caste supremacy in the region. In 1939, this took an extreme form in the concept of Dravida Nadu put forward by E.V. Ramasami Naicker alias the Periyar: "*a homeland for the Dravidians who spoke Telugu, Tamil, Malayalam and Kannada and were racially, ethnically and culturally different from the Aryans of the rest of India*", (Mohan

Ram 1968: 79). In Tamil Nadu and possibly elsewhere in the south, Annadurai's 'Aryan illusion' was something which acted as the focal point of movements against Brahmanical caste orthodoxy and the maintenance of Brahmanical power (for some details, Bergunder 2004). On the other hand, for the Brahmins, that was a major intellectual plank for retaining their position and power.

It should be clear by now that the Aryan hypothesis was never a mere academic concept right from its inception in the late 18th century when it was linked to the politics of the rising British power's necessity to relate India to the history of world civilization, as it was then understood in the light of the Biblical theory of creation. By the middle of the 19th century, with the establishment of the direct imperial rule, India lost her position as a centre of civilization sending out people in the Western direction. It then became far more easy to appreciate India at the receiving end of various migrations from the West, and the notion of a group of horse-riding people penetrating the vast Indian land mass and imposing, as they went along, their superior language and culture on the natives was something which suited very well the intellectual climate of the day. This also fitted perfectly with the racial schemes of the Indian population, which came along during that time and of course, with Max Müller's version of 'the science of language'. The fact that the Indian historians which appeared as a group basically from the last quarter of the 19th century and belonged by and large to the upper castes would gloat over their 'Aryan' identity and kinship with the members of the ruling power was not surprising. What is surprising is that this idea came to be interpreted in various ways by social reform movements in different parts of the country. Whereas Dayananda Saraswati offered the image of an Aryan utopia with the Aryans being the autochthones of the land, J. Phule and others turned this on its head and used it to build up the identity of the lower castes vis-à-vis the upper caste Aryans. In Tamil Nadu, the reaction against the idea led to the consolidation of Dravida identity. Only B.R. Ambedkar, the founder of Dalit movements, could see logically what the idea was worth: a theory "based on nothing but pleasing assumptions and the inferences based on such assumptions".

HOW HAS THE ARYAN NOTION FARED WITHIN THE LAST 50 YEARS IN INDIA AND WHAT IS ITS STATUS NOW?

The examples that we have cited above are all more than 50 years old. In the 1950s and 1960s, with the vastly increased amount of archaeological researches in Indian protohistory, the Indian archaeologists entered the scene in a big way, there being theories galore regarding the archaeological identifications of the Vedic Aryans. They were logically inconsistent, mutually contradictory, and led nowhere (for a review, Chakrabarti 1968). In the books and articles written by powerful Indian historians and archaeologists up to the 1980s, it was considered almost axiomatic that the Painted Grey Ware culture of the upper Ganga plain and the Indo-Gangetic divide (*c.* 1200–700/800 BC) represented the Later Vedic culture. There was no reason why it was more acceptable than many other theories of this type except that B.B. Lal, a prominent Indian archaeologist, propounded it (Lal 1955), and it was accepted by historians like R.S. Sharma (cf. 1985) who was the chief of the Government of India funding body named 'Indian Council of Historical Research'. To some like the present author, the question was why should the pursuit of archaeology in the country be bogged down in the Aryan quagmire and why could not one offer a strictly archaeological version of Indian history.

Since the 1980s the problem has taken a sinister political turn, slowly degenerating into a question of 'progress' versus 'reaction' or the 'secularists' versus 'Hindu fundamentalists'. The background of this development is as follows:

Since the late 18th century, the geographers of the subcontinent have been aware that the Indus River system had a parallel but dried-up river system to its east—from the Siwaliks of modern Haryana to the Rann and the Gulf of Kutch. James Rennell's map of the region in 1788 clearly shows the major channel of this dried-up river system passing through the bordering region of modern Rajasthan and Sind. Named variously in various sectors, this river system is generally known as the Ghaggar-Hakra river system and identified with the course of the Sarasvati which is the most important river mentioned in the *Rigveda*. Despite some doubts to the contrary, this identification is firmly established. The most detailed discussion so far on the drainage lines of the whole of the region from the Siwaliks to the sea was published by H.G. Raverty in 1892. This more than 500-page discussion was based on an exhaustive enumeration of the writings of the early Muslim chroniclers and geographers and also on the results of an unpublished ground survey conducted before 1790.The archaeological potential of this currently arid region has also been understood since the1830s. In the upper part of this river system in modern Haryana, Panjab and Rajasthan archaeological explorations and excavations have brought to light, since the 1950s, a plethora of Indus Civilization and related sites. The full significance of this river stretch remained, however, to be understood till in 1974–77 an exploration on the Pakistani side brought to light a large number of sites belonging to the entire sequential growth, development and decline of the Indus Civilization.

Archaeologists confronted a new reality: the largest concentration of Indus and Indus-related sites was not along the Indus but along its parallel river system to the east, i.e. the river system identified as that of the Sarasvati mentioned in the *Rigveda*. With the induction of remote-sensing techniques in the cause of Indian archaeology, a more detailed knowledge of the course, etc. of this ancient river system is slowly becoming available (for the details of the Sarasvati research, Chakrabarti and Saini 2010, chapter 1; also Danino 2011).

The details of this ongoing research are not the concern of our present discussion. What is important is that this has brought to the fore an old debate: whether the Indus Civilization people could be associated with the composers of the Vedic literature. Considering that the *Rigveda* was composed in the valleys of the Indus and the Sarasvati and considering that only the sites of the Harappan or Indus tradition are found in this region, the correlation between the Vedas and the people of this civilization is certainly not an improbability. A logically strong argument in favour of this proposition has been put forward by B.B. Lal (cf. 2005). On the other hand, those who believe in the Aryan concept with all its trappings are unhappy with such opinions and have gone to the extent of doubting virtually everything that has been written about the Sarasvati since the late18th century. Irfan Habib (2001) seems to be a representative of this school which seems to be ignorant of the fact that this is an old debate going back to the very period when the civilization was discovered and that scholars such as P.V. Kane, M.S. Vats, R.P. Chanda and B.N. Dutta had no problem in accepting a relation between the Harappans and the composers of the Vedas (for the details, Chakrabarti 2008). That an old academic debate is currently given a political shape as a conflict between 'progress' represented by historians like Habib and 'reaction' typified by Hindu fundamentalism is inexplicable.

Equally inexplicable is the fact that in the current Indian historical literature there are two apparently contradictory attitudes to the Aryan issue. On the one hand, scholars such as Romila Thapar, a long-time adherent of Aryan invasion theory, currently try to sanitise the notion by taking all racial implications out of it (Thapar 2007 reprint), and on the other, there are scholars such as D.N. Jha (1998), a former general president of the Indian History Congress, who finds in them a 'distinct physical appearance'.

Thus, the Aryan hypothesis that we find in most history books on India is not an innocuous academic concept, just as it is not in the context of Europe and elsewhere.

REFERENCES

Aiyangar, S. Krishnaswami. 1923. *Some Contributions of South India to Indian Culture.* Calcutta

Ambedkar, B.R. 1970 reprint. *Who were the Sudras?* Bombay.

Anthony, D.W. 2007. *The Horse, the Wheel and Language, How Bronze-Age Riders from the Eurasian Steppes Shaped the Modern World.* Princeton.

Arvidsson, S. 2006. *Aryan Idols, Indo-European Mythology as Ideology and Science.* Chicago.

Barnett, M.D. 1976. *The Politics of Cultural Nationalism in South India.* Princeton.

Barrow, R. 1789. A Proof That the Hindus Had Binominal Theorem. *Asiatic Researches* 2: 487-97.

Bergunder, M. 2004. Contested Past, Anti-Brahmanical and Hindu Nationalist Reconstructions of Indian Prehistory. *Historigraphia Linguistica* 31: 59-104.

Bharadwaja, C. 1927. *Light of Truth or an English Translation of the Satyarth Prakash.* Lahore.

Chakrabarti, D.K. 1968. The Aryan hypothesis in Indian Archaeology. *Indian Studies: Past and Present* 9: 343-58.

—. 1976a. India and the Druids. *Antiquity* 50: 66-67.

—. 1976b. The Beginning of Iron in India. *Antiquity* 50: 114-24.

—. 1988. *A History of Indian Archaeology from the Beginning to 1947.* Delhi.

—. 1997. *Colonial Indology. Sociopolitics of the Ancient Indian Past.* Delhi.

—. 2008. *The Battle for Ancient India.* Delhi.

Chakrabarti, D.K. and Sukhdev Saini. 2009. *The Problem of the Sarasvati River, and Notes on the Archaeological Geography of Haryana and Indian Panjab.* Delhi.

Deshpande, G.P. (ed.). 2002. *Selected Writings of Jotirao Phule.* Delhi.

Diamond, J. and P. Bellwood. 2003. Farmers and Their Languages: The First Expansions. *Science* 300(5619): 597-603.

Habib, I. 2001. Imaging River Saraswati: A Defence of Commonsense. *Social Scientist* 29: 46-74.

Iyengar, Shesha, T.R. 1925. *Dravidian India.* Vol.1. Madras.

Jha, D.N. 1998. *Ancient India in Historical Outline.* Delhi.

Jordens, J.T.F. 1978. *Dayananda Sarasvati, His Life and Ideas.* Delhi.

Lal, B.B. 1955. Excavations at Hastinapura. *Ancient India* 10 & 11: 6-151.

—. 2002. *The Saraswati Flows On: The Continuity of Indian Culture.* Delhi.

—. 2005. *In Search of the Aryan Homeland, the Continuation of a Debate.* Delhi.

Lincoln, B. 1999. *Theorizing Myth, Narrative, Ideology, and Scholarship.* Chicago.

Londo, J.P. et al. 2006. Phylogeography of Asian wild rice, Oryza rupifogon, reveals multiple independent domestications of cultivated rice. *Proceedings of the national Academy of Sciences USA* 103 (25): 9578-83.

Meadow, R. and A. Patel. 1997. A Comment on "Horse Remains from Surkotada" by Sandor Bokonyi. *South Asian Studies* 13: 308-15.

Mitra, R.L. 1858. Buddhism and Odinism, Their Similitude. *Journal of the Asiatic Society of Bengal* 28: 46-69.

Muir, J. 1872. Reprint. *Original Sanskrit Texts on the Origin and History of the People of India, Their Religion and Institutions/ Collected, Translated and Illustrated by J. Muir*. London.

O'Hanlon, R. 1985. *Caste, Conflict and Ideology. Mahatma Jotirao Phule and Low Caste Protest in Nineteenth Century Western India*. Cambridge.

Poliakov, L. 1974. *The Aryan Myth: A History of Racism and Nationalist Ideas in Europe*. London.

Ram, Mohan 1968. *Hindi against India, the Meaning of DMK.* Delhi.

Rao, L.S. 2005-2006. The Harappan spoked wheel rattled down the streets of Bhirrana, district Fatehabad, Haryana. *Puratattva* 36: 59-67.

Sharma, R.S. 1985. *Material Culture and Social Formations in Ancient India.* Delhi.

——. 2003. *Advent of the Aryans in India.* Delhi.

Slater, G. 1924 *The Dravidian Element in Indian Culture*. London.

Tewari, Rakesh. 2003. Origins of Iron-Working in India: New Evidence from the Central Ganga Plain and the Eastern Vindhyas. *Antiquity* 77: 536-44.

Tewari, Rakesh et al. 2004. Archaeological Studies in Lohuradeva Area, Implications, Ganga Plain. *Abstract*. Lucknow, pp. 59-60.

Thapar, R. et al. 2007. Reprint. *India: Historical Beginnings and the Concept of the Aryan.* Delhi.

7

Amused by Hinduism: *The Ancient South Asian World* by

J.M. KENOYER AND KIMBERLEY HEUSTON

The Ancient South Asian World is jointly authored by J.M. Kenoyer, the recent (2011) 'Presidential lecturer' of the Indian Archaeological Society, and Kimberley Heuston, an educationist based in New York, and was published by the Oxford University Press, New York in 2005. This was the book to which a section of the USA-based Hindu community, especially the group settled in California, objected to being accepted as a textbook in Californian schools without incorporating the changes they listed in detail with the help of Professor Siva Bajpai, a respected Indian scholar of ancient Indian history in California. This call for change in a book which was written by a pillar of the American establishment in the field of ancient India opened a veritable Pandora's box of dispute and constituted what came to be known later as California Text Book Controversy (CTBC). I was not involved in this controversy in any way but I could keep a general eye, thanks to the worldwide web, on how the controversy was shaping up. It appears that the controversy is now over, and this may be the time when I can permit myself some comments on the book itself.

Regarding Kenoyer's position in the American academic establishment in the field of ancient India, let me point out that he has emerged in the past decade as the West's principal scholar of the Indus Civilization. Among other things, he was especially invited to give a lecture on the Indus Civilization at the Institute of Archaeology of London University, and after the lecture a formal dinner was organized by the Institute in his honour. On a separate occasion, he was invited by the MacDonald Institute for Archaeological Research, Cambridge, to one of its seminars to speak on the linear measurements and weight system of the Indus Civilization, although I suggested the name of S. Kak of Louisiana for the purpose. In the forthcoming volume on world prehistory/archaeology of the Cambridge University Press, the Indus Civilization is interpreted for us by him.Those of us who suffer from the delusion that the opinion of the subcontinentals matters in the domain of Indus scholarship are likely to be pained to know that it does not matter at all. The list of books/articles recommended in the various Western academic courses on the Indus Civilization is enough to prove my point. The recent Cambridge University Press publication on the Indus Civilization by Rita Wright, a book which I think is 'colour-coded' in its approach to scholarship, was not submitted for manuscript review to any native South Asia specialist in Britain. If what I am told is correct, Kenoyer has been given access by the Archaeological Survey of India to different types of excavated material from Dholavira. Kenoyer has long been actively involved, along with his Indian 'satellites', in trying to set up an Indus Centre either in Pune or in Vadodara with the help of an American NGO called Global

Heritage Fund which, reputedly, also draws upon the help of US-based NRIs like Navin Doshi or museum professionals like Kalpana Desai. The point I am making is that J.M. Kenoyer is not merely a renowned scholar in the eyes of our colleagues in Pune / Vadodara or the Archaeological Survey of India but also in the estimate of the British universities like London and Cambridge and some America-based NRIs.

The book, as the publisher's advertisement tells us, "uses primary sources and lively details to bring to life the landscape and people of ancient south Asia". It uses "artefacts and archaeological sites as a framework for the exploration of the history of the region from the first cities of the Indus to the golden age of the Gupta Empire".

I am not sure if I can find much of primary source in the book. Chapter 11, for instance, describes "fire and sacrifice, living by the Vedas" but does not mention the particular portion of the Vedic texts from which the description derives. It is very much a generalized description according to the authors' understanding. The chapter is also interesting in the archaeological sense because it highlights the authors' notion of the archaeology of the subcontinent after the Indus Civilization. I shall examine the authors' archaeological sense later in this discussion. In Chapter 12 which deals with the epic traditions of the *Mahabharata* and the *Ramayana*, the texts are dated straightaway without mentioning how these were dated and what are the pitfalls of such dating. More problematic are cultural assertions like the following. The *Mahabharata* is supposedly "a historical document that tells us a lot about the Vedic communities at the end of the Vedic Era". What is the 'Vedic Era' and which 'Vedic communities' are the authors talking about here? Unsupported assertions like these are abundant throughout the text: around

1000 BCE, "the Vedic rituals practised by the Brahmins began to change. Earlier traditions of the Indus Civilization and other local beliefs began to creep back into use." How do the authors reach this date and offer this explanation? On p. 90 it is asserted that "the Brahmanical religion grew up along the banks of the Ganga River", but does this mean that other parts of the country contributed nothing to the development of this religion? The authors are silent on this point. Or take the case of the following comment: "Shiva was not the only deity that people began paying more attention to about 1000 BCE". The authors are supposed to depend on archaeology. Does archaeology suggest what they have written about Shiva? The true measure of the authors' attitude to Hinduism comes a little later (p. 93):

> The earlier Vedic religion was changing. Animal sacrifices were being replaced with butter and fruit offerings, new deities were emphasized instead of Agni and Brahma, and people could not move between the *varnas* at all. In time, these new practices became known as Hinduism.

One did not know if such clear-cut evolutionary characterisations of Hindu religion were possible. The authors' attitude to Hinduism is clear from their comment (p. 93) that it is not "so much a single unified religion as a family of religious traditions". The overarching framework of monism, an essential element of Sanatana Dharma is here completely ignored by them.

I am somewhat amazed by the book. Contrary to the publisher's claim, it does not even try to offer any geographical and archaeological perspective to the Indian civilization. Their sense of Indian history is manifest in their assertion that the Buddhist king Asoka's prohibition of animal sacrifice upset Brahmins who in turn "convinced the leaders of one region after another to break away from the Mauryan empire after Ashoka's death" (p. 123). The authors do not specify if they have any dependable relevant source or are simply using their historical imagination. On p. 102 they further tell us that Asoka made Buddhism "the state religion of his empire". Was it the state religion in the sense that Islam is in Pakistan or Christianity is in Britain? As far as I understand it, Asoka would not have been what he was if he had felt the necessity of having a 'state religion'.

I think I have written enough to underscore the general level of this book as a historical and archaeological exercise. In the documents I have had access to regarding the CTBC, Dr. A. Rambachan, a professor of religion in an American institution, raises this question of the general level of this book, and I consider it important to quote him here:

The following is a review of the Hinduism section of this book (pp. 77-95 only).

"1. Assumes the historical truth of the disputed Aryan Invasion theory (p. 76).
2. In its description of the curriculum of an ancient Vedic school (p. 78) it suggests that the caste system would be among the first subjects taught. What is the basis of this claim?
3. Wrongly equates the Shudras of ancient India with the untouchables (p. 79)
4. While describing the "major Gods and Goddesses of the Vedas", it makes no mention of the more complex idea that these are understood as expressions of one (*Rigveda*: *Ekam Sat Viprah Bahudha Vadanti*).
5. At various points in the text the authors seem to think it necessary to interject supposedly humourous comments into the main narrative (eg. p. 85 and p. 87). In the last reference,

the authors mention the Hindu belief that Hanuman is present whenever the *Ramayana* is recited. After mentioning this the text comments: "So look around—see any monkeys?". What is the point of this exercise? Is it to debunk the faith claim of the Hindu believer? Is it cheap form of humour?

6. In its discussion of reincarnation, text refers to the possibility of rebirth as a chicken, pig or fish (p. 88). While there are indeed texts that are open to the possibility of rebirth in animal forms, this is not all that reincarnation is about, Unfortunately this seems to be the emphasis in most texts. The more comprehensive character of reincarnation as a moral law is ignored.
7. Multiplicity of gods listed (p. 90-91) without any clarification of Hindu pluralism—the belief that One may be named and represented in many ways."

Professor Rambachan's assertion that the authors subscribe to the Aryan invasion theory is clear from their discussion on p. 78: about 2000 BCE one "would see spaces opening up in the jungles along the Yamuna and Ganga River Valley as new communities moved in. These communities cut down and burned trees to make room for towns, cities and fields of summer crop watered by the monsoon, such as rice and millet". This page also gives the impression that there was no earlier settlement worth taking about in the Ganga-Yamuna Plain. This impression is completely wrong as hundreds of settlements in modern western Uttar Pradesh stretching up to the Siwaliks indicate. The date of the earliest level of Alamgirpur is about the middle of the third millennium BC. Also, how do the authors know that opening up jungles along the Ganga and the Yamuna by cutting down and burning tress was initiated around 2000 BC? As Rakesh Tewari has shown, the Ganga-Yamuna Plain of the period was not necessarily full of trees or jungles before this date. More importantly, the authors openly acknowledge their belief in the Aryan invasion /migration theory by writing that "we know a lot more about these new communities than we do the about the Harappans because we have their scripture, called the Vedas" (p. 77). In this light, Kenoyer's written admission to Mr. Navin Dosi (email dated 28 November, 2005, with copy to Kalpana Desai) that he does "not support the views of an Indo-Aryan invasion of South Asia as there is no archaeological or as far as I can see literary or physical evidence for this type of event " does not seem to bear any relationship with the truth. Further, in his essay in a book edited by Romila Thapar in 2006/2007 *India: Historical Beginning and the Concept of the Aryan* (Delhi: National Book Trust), Kenoyer does not seem to repudiate his belief in the Aryans.

Many elements of Hinduism seem to provide occasions for merriment to the authors. Professor Rambachan has cited only the example related to *Hanuman-ji* whose temple—Sankatmochan temple—I visit as a believer when I go to Varanasi and Delhi. There are also other cases in the book. This, however, is entirely according to the authors' taste. Academics at least usually avoid revealing their attitude to other people's religion as far as they can help it. If the authors have violated this code, that was for their publisher to decide. On my part I do not find anything original or historically clear in this volume. Nor do I find it difficult to ignore if my religion is caricatured. I am aware that this is much more deeply rooted in the Indian soil than the authors of this book are capable of thinking. Further, as the book *Invading the Sacred: An Analysis of Hinduism Studies in America*

(K. Ramaswamy, A. Nicolas and A. Banerjee (eds.), Delhi 2007: Rupa) has clearly demonstrated, having some fun at the expense of Hinduism has long been—and still is—an established academic practice in the West. So, the attitude displayed by the Kenoyer-Heuston volume is hardly a matter of surprise. What is also worthy of note that this attitude which may be described as 'Hindu-baiting' is of no concern to Kenoyer's collaborators in Pune, Vadodara and elsewhere! Of one thing, however, one can be positive. Books like this are no stuff from which young people should learn history, and the Americans of Indian origin who questioned the appropriateness of its being included in the Californian school syllabus were entirely right in doing so.

8

A Colour-coded Perception of Scholarship?

RITA P. WRIGHT AND THE STUDY OF THE INDUS CIVILIZATION

Rita P. Wright is an Associate Professor of Anthropology at New York University and a member of the archaeological research group which is centred around the prolonged American excavations at Harappa. Her *The Ancient Indus: Urbanism, Economy and Society* (Cambridge 2010: Cambridge University Press) incorporates many already-published ideas of this group. It may be important for Indian archaeologists to understand what these ideas are and what are their implications. One of her opening comments is that "scholarship on the Indus civilization has lagged behind that of Mesopotamia and Egypt" (p. 1). Archaeological research in these two areas began well above a hundred years earlier than the date of the discovery of the Indus Civilization and also possesses a rich literary texture which is missing in the Indus context because of the un-deciphered character of its script. Besides, much of the interpretation of the Indus finds and the world of the Indus rituals, beliefs, technology and artistic expressions, is based on their continuation and survivals in historic and even present India. The Indus scholarship, from this viewpoint alone, is vastly different from the Egyptian and Mesopotamian situations. Comparisons between the two types of research traditions are not valid. Another opening statement of the book (p. 2) is that the Indus Civilization is known as Meluhha in the Mesopotamian documents. It is an interesting possibility, but despite being repeated *ad finitum*, it is not an impeccable academic conclusion. Once I pointed out the pitfalls of this assumption by pointing out I. Gelb's opinion on the general uncertainties of the various explanations of the ancient Mesopotamian geographical and other terms, but that cut no ice with the scholars, determinedly bent on making a productive academic career out of Indus-Mesopotamia contact. I still refuse to believe that Meluhha means more than the general areas to the east of Mesopotamian civilization. Professor Wright passes rather hurriedly over the story of the Indus discovery, leading occasionally to wrong observations. For instance, Alexander Cunningham was not 'trained in Sanskrit' and his interests went far beyond 'only numismatics and archaeology' (p. 7). R.D. Banerji in his now-published report on the results of his excavations at Mohenjo-daro makes rather funny comments regarding his finds, and I hesitate to accept that he understood the broad significance of his finds at the site. What is really striking and ignored by Professor Wright is that Alexander Cunningham in the first volume of *Corpus Inscriptionum Indicarum* in1877 linked the origin of the historical Brahmi script with the script on the seals from Harappa which he recorded, although only from the surface. Stuart Piggott was trained in British archaeology (and not in Classical archaeology, as Professor Wright argues), and his main contribution to Indian proto-historic studies lay, like Gordon Childe before him, in grouping Aurel Stein's Baluchistan material into 'cultures' in terms of their similarities with the painted pottery tradition of Iran and elsewhere. The British-Indian excavations at the Indus sites had no 'political dimension' (p. 11) and the argument that these excavations "served to create an image of a common heritage for the vast territory encompassed by British India" (p. 11) is unacceptable. The discovery of the Indus Civilization was only 23 years earlier than the end of the British rule of the country, and the British then could not have any ambition of archaeologically pointing out its common heritage. On the other hand, opinion such as this implies that the idea of a common heritage of the subcontinent is, according to scholars like Professor Wright, a mere political device. I also doubt if Mortimer Wheeler can be accused of importing 'militaristic imperialism' to the Indus studies because his excavations yielded 'citadels', 'bastions', 'defences' and 'gateways' at Harappa (p. 12). Do the critics have better terms for these structural features of this site or, for that matter, many other excavated Indus civilization sites? *The examples of 'new' research on the Indus issues in this book are all products of Euro-American research and have no place for Pakistani and Indian archaeologists.* I do not find the author's definition of 'civilization', 'city' and 'urbanism' (pp. 13-15) particularly illuminating, or even necessary in this case except to emphasize the special anthropological orientation of the work. There is also emphasis on the desirability of working out a relationship between 'city' and 'countryside'. The point that the early states did not control everything has been made with examples from Africa, Mesopotamia, Maya and even Vijayanagara, but who on earth ever assumed that that the historical state structures did not leave any space for individual productive organizations? Many non-Vijayanagara Indian inscriptions also carry unequivocal references to the role played by trade organizations and local councils in various administrative arrangements. In the section on 'theoretical perspectives' the professed focus of interest is "the infra-structural arrangements behind Indus agriculture, pastoralism and craft-production, its landscape construction and urban forms, and its human-landscape interrelations". Right in the beginning (p. 20) it has been argued that the Harappan craftsmen did something remarkably innovative by grinding down stones to malleable pastes for the production of ornaments and inscribed devices and enhancing the colour of stones by heating them. What is not answered is whether these techniques figured for the first time in the Indus context or had precedence in various and diverse pre-and-non-Harappan contexts.Issues such as "cities as places of memory, identity, etc." are mentioned, but again, it is not pointed out that, without the help of texts, assertions such as these will always remain unsubstantiated. A major theoretical concern of the book has been said to emphasize "the interconnected nature of the Greater Near East and the Indus". The implication is that the Indus Civilization has to be understood not as a part of a continuous Indian tradition but as an extension of the 'Greater Near East' (whatever that may mean) up to the Indus. This spells out the theoretical orientation of the author in far sharper detail than all the other 'goals' she has mentioned in the opening section of her work. There is a section on the "key transformative points in the development of the Indus Civilization" towards the end of the first chapter. The early food-production is supposed to begin around 6300 BC, whereas according to the Mehrgarh chronology, it should be *c.* 7000 BC. This reviewer is confused by this, just as he is confused by the complete silence over the fact that the radiocarbon chronology which is offered may admit of variations and disagreements, and that in the case of the mature urban phase at least, the radiocarbon evidence is not wholly supported by the historical evidence of Indus-Mesopotamia contact. This reviewer is also puzzled by the somewhat glib assertion that in the Late Harappan period "settlements shifted toward the northeast to the Ghaggar Plain away from the Indus Valley toward northeast India and Gujarat". *In view of the dates which have emerged from Bhirrana, Farmana and many sites from Gujarat and have placed these areas in the core zone of the Indus Civilization, such a claim of shift from the Indus valley to modern Rajasthan, Haryana, Panjab and Gujarat is completely unacceptable. The idea that the Indus Valley alone constitutes the core area of the Indus Civilization seems to be a crucial assumption of the book.* What is called the Ghaggar Plain (as opposed to the Hakra Plain of Pakistan) is a vast stretch of land in Rajasthan, Haryana, Panjab and western Uttar Pradesh, which extends up to the Siwaliks, and there is no reason to assume that the growth of Indus settlements of this zone had necessarily to wait for shifts of population from the Indus River side. Chapter 2 is on "geographical and environmental settings". Various current theories regarding the moist-aridity cycle of climate in the concerned region is cited, but no specific attention is given to Y. Enzell's opinion that "the Indus civilization flourished mainly along rivers during times when northwestern India experienced semiarid climatic conditions that are similar to those at present". The evidence that the Hakra groundwater was not recharged after 3000/2700 BC seems to be a major argument in its favour. Whatever nineteenth century and earlier historic evidence the present reviewer has been able to study in the case of Haryana and Panjab in his *The Problem of the Sarasvati River and Notes on the Archaeological Geography of Haryana and Indian Panjab* (Delhi 2009: Aryan Books; co-author: S. Saini) seems to suggest that the Indus Civilization sites could flourish in this region even without arguing a case for greater rainfall. A 10th century historical text calls in fact the Yaudheya country or the modern Haryana-Panjab sector 'an ornament of the earth' where the abundance of irrigation rendered it free from the vagaries of rain. Professor Wright prefers to ignore the vast body of literature which has been accumulating on the Ghaggar-Hakra course since the late 18th century. This would have shown her the complexity of the river system which ran parallel with the Indus to the east and encompassed an equally large, if not a larger area. There can be no worthwhile discussion on the geographical and environmental setting of the Indus Civilization without taking the details of this region into consideration. Regrettably Professor Wright preferred to confine herself to the oscillatory curves of the climatic charts and some inane climatic and agricultural reconstructions (cf. those by Fuller and Madella, Weber). In recent years the fluctuations of the Indian summer monsoon have been studied alongwith a straight-jacketed view of their archaeological impacts by A.K. Gupta and his associates, but this literature does not find any place in the present author's discussions, although the author and the group led by Gupta both seem to prefer a straight-jacketed approach to the impact of climate on culture. It would, however, be wrong not to draw attention to Professor Wright's fine study of the distribution of Indus-related sites along an old bed of the Beas (fig. 2.1). Chapter 3 is entitled "From Foraging to Farming and Pastoralism", with Mehrgarh as the central point. The author knows the site well and is thoroughly familiar with its data through all periods. She is also aware that there could be multiple centres of cattle domestication in India. What she does not lay enough emphasis on is the fact that in India there could be multiple centres of agricultural origins as well. Mehrgarh was within the nuclear centre of barley domestication. Regarding wheat the opinion is not unequivocal; it could receive its impetus of wheat cultivation from the areas further west. The cultivation of rice came up in the central Ganga Plain and the adjacent Vindhyas as early as the 7th millennium BC, and the fact that rice occurs in the Early Harappan context at places like Kunal and Balu in Haryana shows that the agricultural system of the Indus Civilization was not exclusively related to Mehrgarh or the Baluchistan area. In a number of publications the present reviewer has argued the probable role of the Aravalli region too in this context, and the significance of the central Ganga Plain, of course, stands undisputed. The point is that the growth of the Indus Civilization was not a linear development of what took place in the Kachi plain of Baluchistan in *c.* 7000 BC. Multiple courses of development, including the developments which took place in the central Ganga Plain and the Aravallis, led up to it. Radiocarbon dates from Tokwa near Halia in Uttar Pradesh show the presence of wheat and barley in a Neolithic context as early as 7000/6000 BC, and as Tokwa cannot be within the primary area of wheat-barley cultivation, one has to accept the idea of wheat-barley agricultural dispersal from Baluchistan to the heart of India soon after their cultivation began in Baluchistan. These Tokwa dates will remain inexplicable till more dates are obtained and the evidence is sorted out. However, this shows that the story of India's agricultural beginnings is not yet fully settled. Interestingly, one need not envisage the existence of a wetter climate to explain the growth of settlement at Mehrgarh. The vegetation has not changed within the last ten millennia, and even in the second half of the nineteenth century Mehrgarh was in an agriculturally prosperous region. Chapter 4 deals with the period before full urban growth and is called "an era of expansion and transformation". This is basically a start-up of the sequence leading up to the Indus Civilization and its transformation, and the author dubs it as "an age of emerging polities" based on a set of twelve features including the presence of settlements having different functions and the creation of communicative systems through written symbols and the precursors of urban seals. The chronological baseline adopted for this phase is *c.* 3500/3300 BC, although the spread of agricultural settlements with specialized crafts throughout the Indus-Ghaggar alluvium and Gujarat and western Uttar Pradesh is likely to date comfortably from the 5th millennium BC. There are dates from this range from the Hakra ware level at Bhirrana, but even otherwise, when one thinks of the effectively rooted character of the distribution of the Hakra/Ravi villages and the level of their crafts, one has to assume that this must have taken a few centuries to evolve. The extent to which the process was helped by parallel early agricultural developments in the Aravallis and central Ganga Plain also remains to be seen. In any case, the author's emphasis in this section is on the development at Harappa which she can delineate with confidence and in detail. The evidence of writing and seals that she reports from the Early Harappan phase of the site has been duplicated, as far as the present reviewer is aware, at Padri, Dholavira and Kunal, showing that over a very large region, way beyond the Indus, there was a steady development towards civilization and statehood. In fact, taking writing as the distinguishing feature of civilization, there is no reason why the urban status should be denied to the Early Harappans. An important part of this chapter is a brief section on the "upper Indus regional surveys near Harappa". By this time one may confidently assume a wide exchange network of both finished goods and raw materials throughout the relevant region. In the section on "pre-urban ecological and settlement diversity" (p. 102) the author speaks of the beginning of irrigation in Baluchistan in *c.* 3500 BC. The author argues that peoples' "experiments with water-retaining devices" began around that period. Here the author forgets a simple point to which the present reviewer has drawn attention on a number of occasions. Canal irrigation had been practised in the pre-industrial agriculture of Sindh where rice was the most important crop, and looking at even sites like Mehrgarh in Baluchistan, one feels, especially in view of the unchanged character of the vegetation of the area since proto-history, that agriculture was impossible in an area with 3 or 4 inches of annual rainfall without some kind of irrigation. The Kachi Plain is an area of roughly 15000 sq. km, drained by a few rivers and a host of hill torrents. As I pointed out in 2006 *(The Oxford Companion to Indian Archaeology*, p. 107), "on entering the Kachi plain these hill torrents dissipate into countless natural channels. The pre-modern system of irrigation was to raise the flood water of such channels by throwing barriers across them, with the consequent overflow going to the fields". Irrigation must have been known long before the date offered by the author. Chapter 5 is titled "urbanism and states: cities, regions and edge zones" and deals with the Indus cities in all their distribution areas. The distribution and morphology of the urban settlements have been made clear, although places like Juni Kuran in Kutch or structural features such as a stadium at Dholavira and two such structures at Juni Kuran find no mention here. A few major excavated sites from Gujarat as a whole are missing too. There is no reason to call the stupa of Mohenjo-daro 'so-called stupa' because Verardi's doubt of the identification spring from uncertain data and possible keenness to find something similar to Sumerian ziggurat at Mohenjo-daro. The section on "the upper

Indus and Beas regional surveys near Harappa (pp. 127-31) contains some local details and are useful from that point of view. Of similar importance is the section on "the lower Indus regional surveys" (pp. 134-36). The author argues (p. 138) that "the Indus cities were organized into several city states loosely integrated by a common material culture". In my *The Archaeology of Ancient Indian Cities* (Delhi 1995; p. 273 of the1997 paperback edition) I disputed the idea of a homogeneous Harappan empire: "on the contrary, if we look at the later political history of the entire region, we are likely to argue in favour of the idea of a number of separate kingdoms throughout the Harappan distribution zone". The idea has been subsequently elaborated in a number of my publications. The functional role of each Harappan settlement has to be judged closely in terms of its location in the context of the local geography and the roles of similarly located settlements in later contexts. As far as Lothal dock is concerned, the find of marine organisms within the enclosure conclusively proves it to be a dock. The chapters 6 and 7 are basically on the Indus crafts and based on the knowledge of techniques through replication of the material by the village craftsmen of the area and beyond. In addition, there are sections on individual raw materials and their incorporation in the productive system. It is not that this knowledge did not previously exist; many gazetteers of British India incorporate sections on the local crafts including their production techniques in detail. Similarly, a detailed study of the distribution of the various raw materials used in the Indus context and the light it throws on the Indus trade routes was published in 1992 by Nayanjot Lahiri. The non-mention of a major source of tin in the Tosam area of Haryana is somewhat surprising, and on the basis of Professor C. Lamberg-Karlovsky's observation, one may say that tin occurs also somewhere in the Quetta region. Chapter 7 is on internal and external trade. The details of the related finds have been given, although the Mesoptamian textual portions should have been mentioned as being largely speculative. Traditional trade has always been conducted in the concerned areas, with the Indus trade laying down the first visible point of this continuum. The nineteenth century documentation of this trade is easily accessible and throws light both on how the trade was carried out and what were the commodities traded. The Gilund decorative seal impressions have nothing to do with the BMAC seals. In The *Oxford Companion* (p. 231) I pointed out that the BMAC seals, as opposed to the Gilund specimens, are mostly metallic and they cover a very wide time-range. Further, the Gilund designs are not exactly identical with the BMAC designs. Chapter 9 is titled " landscapes of order and difference—the cultural construction of space, place and social difference". Much of it is speculative but tries to offer insights. In the case of Mohenjo-daro, it is based mostly on M.Jansen's work. The concept of the 'Axes of Relative Value' (p. 248) offers no insight, and in the case of Ardeleanu-Jansen's reconstruction of the priest-king image, it has to be added that it is entirely speculative and may with ease be ignored. The burials have been put forward as ' landscapes of memory' and the present reviewer has gleaned several new pieces of information from the author's discussion of them.Chapter 10 is on "models for Indus religious ideologies". The belief that "Marshall had in mind to locate a 'state' religion" (p. 276) is surprising because Marshall studied India long enough to know that in the pre-Muslim context there never was a state religion in India, with the individual rulers showing their predilection in various ways. The author does not seem to be happy with Marshall's interpretation of the evidence of Indus religion in the light of later Hindu beliefs and practices. Interestingly, there is no mention of the terracotta *Sivalinga* from Kalibangan in this book. The detailed recent study of the Indus terracottas cannot be said to have yielded any particularly valuable insight. The section on cross-cultural comparisons of the Indus seal imagery with the Mesopotamian and Iranian seal imageries is useful on a general level. There can be any number of philosophical speculations on that basis but whether they bear any relationship with the reality is a different matter altogether. Chapter 11 deals with "the decline and transformation and the comparative study of early states". The relevant archaeological data from the various regions are mustered, leading to, among others, the conclusion that "several strategic shifts in agriculture and pastoralism occurred in the post-urban period" (p. 321). It is not specifically clear how this has been inferred. How do they know, for instance, that the cultivation of 'summer millets and rice' became more widespread in the post-urban context? Further, what is the great significance of crop-processing in this context? Has not the primary focus of crop-processing in India been always the individual households? Premises such as these may satisfy the researchers' scientific propensity to find things in a logical linear order, especially if the researchers concerned do not know the local language in which their subjects conduct their lives, but do they carry any academic value? The concluding sections of the book carry a lot of such observations and inferences. There will naturally be a lot of areas in which one specialist student will differ from another. I have drawn attention to some of these differences I have with the author, but to be honest, these are not major areas of my concern. I am seriously concerned with the attitude to the Indus Civilization this book represents. Occasional references have no doubt been made to some elements of this civilization which have continued in later Indian contexts, but that is an aberration rather than the norm in this book. To this reviewer the Indus Civilization is the fountainhead of the later Indian 'high' tradition, besides the continuation of various technologies and beliefs in the Indian countryside. To the author of this book that is of no concern or academic use. Equally interestingly, I find a strong 'separation' between the author's bibliography at the end of the book, which is a somewhat arbitrary list of writings on Indian archaeology, and the references cited in the text, which are, almost exclusively, Euro-American. The examples and the opinions cited are similarly dependent on Euro-American scholarship. The inescapable conclusion is that this is a book on the Indus Civilization written by an American scholar for the fellow Euro-American or White scholars. The native scholarship on this civilization does not have any place here just as the native Iraqi or Egyptian scholarship is by and large absent in the books on ancient Iraq and Egypt written by the Western scholars. The perception of scholarship in this regard is obviously 'colour-coded', and I find it regrettable that this 'colour-coded' perception of scholarship has made a serious entry in Indian archaeology, as this book and many other publications of this genre indicate. The First World archaeology carries within it more strands of 'colour-coding' than it knows in relation to the Third World archaeologists.

9

Cultural Unity of India

The Evidence of Archaeology and Historical Geography

One of the most visible signs of early contact between different parts of India is the spread of objects which are either identical in form and manufacture or possess undeniable family resemblance over large parts of the country. From this point of view, the period of the Indus Civilization is as good a meaningful period as any. First, the objects of this civilization are distributed from Baluchistan-Iran border to roughly Haridwar and from Jammu to the Kim estuary in Gujarat and further south in Maharashtra. This distribution is most noticeable during the mature and late phases of the Indus Civilization, i.e. roughly from *c.* 2700 to 1300 BC. Secondly, the material needs of this civilization threw open many resource areas both within and outside its distribution zone and led to the development of various routes, many of which retained their significance in later periods. For instance, there was a clear alignment in the Indus period between the Dera Ghazi Khan and Dera Ismail Khan sector in the northwest and Rohtak in the Delhi sector. The route came via Multan, Harappa, Pakpattan, Abohar, Sirsa, Hansi, and Hissar, throwing offshoots all along the way. One of these offshoots touched Bhatinda, and even now a major bridge near the Bhatinda fort is called Multani bridge. The Rohtak-Hansi-Hissar-Sirsa-Fazilka-Abohar alignment was a major alignment in the historic period as well. The significance of the Indus period in mobilizing and channelizing both the raw materials and finished goods is well understood. Among other things, the finished cores made of the chert of the Sukkur-Rorhi Hills in Sind can be traced at Balu in Jind in Haryana. There need not be any doubt about the fact that the vast area in which Indus Civilization sites have been found evolved a network of interconnection between its component parts.

It is equally important to know how the Indus distribution area was interacting with the areas outside it. The occurrence of a late Harappan occupational level at Daimabad (Sali 1986) is a pointer in this direction. In another direction, the find of perforated ware of Indus tradition at Ramnagar on the bank of the Ganga opposite Banaras is mind-boggling, but the identification was done at the most competent level and there is apparently no reason to doubt it (personal information from R. Tewari).

The significance of the occurrence of the Indus script at Daimabad in the upper Godavari Valley and that of perforated ware at Ramnagar in the middle Ganga Valley are worth pondering over. Considering that at the other end the Indus artefacts are found in Baluchistan and Jammu, there was apparently an interconnecting orbit from this northern limit to the upper Godavari Valley and the middle Ganga Plain as far south as Banaras during the late phase of the Indus Civilization. Daimabad is Late Harappan and the chalcolithic context in which the Harappan perforated ware has been found at Ramnagar belongs to the local chalcolithic context well within the second millennium BC.

A comparatively recent archaeological discovery has considerably highlighted this orbit. In the excavations at Sinoli, a presumably Late Harappan site near Baghpat (Sharma, Nauriyal and Prabhakar 2005-6), a copper antennae-hilted sword has been found, proving that the upper Gangetic Valley 'Copper Hoard 'tradition is linked with the Late Harappan tradition. I would put Sinoli around the middle of the second millennium BC. Such 'antennae-hilted swords' have been found in Gujarat on the west and the Ramanathapuram district of Tamil Nadu and the Tea/Coffee plantation belt of Kerala in the south (the details in Chakrabarti and Lahiri 1996). This is remarkable because this shows that as early as the middle of the second millennium BC there is archaeological evidence that the Doab region was linked with west India and the deep south. I am not enthusiastic about the find of a Neolithic celt with Indus signs pecked into its surface from Cuddalore south of Pondicherry but the antennae-hilted copper swords have been found along a well-known stretch of the Ganga Plain-Deccan – south India route, and there is no reason to doubt the significance of these finds. Because of its being part of the Harappan tradition, the Doab area must have known also the western areas of the Harappan distribution belt up to Panjab, Sind and Baluchistan. Whether the concept of Bharatavarsha was there or not, the people were then certainly interacting over a vast stretch of the land which came to be called Bharatavarsha in literature. Tentatively, I would accept the chronological line of the mid-second millennium BC as a benchmark line in this regard.

As far as the dissemination of cultivated crops is concerned, interesting data have begun to emerge in the case of wheat, barley and rice.

Wheat and barley occur in the 8th millennium BC at Mehrgarh south of Quetta in Baluchistan. Both these crops occur in the Neolithic level of Jhusi (Pokharia 2009) opposite Allahabad. The dates from this level of Jhusi fall in the 8th and 6th millennia BC. This is supported by at least one early date from the Neolithic level of Tokwa (Pokharia 2008) near Mirzapur. On the other hand, the cultivation of rice began in central Ganga plain and the adjacent Vindhyan stretch in the 8th-6th millennia BC with its crucial evidence coming from Lohuradeva near Gorakhpur, Koldihawa and Chopani Mando in the periphery of the Vindhyas near Allahabad, and Jhusi in Allahabad itself (for Lohuradeva,, Tewari et al. 2007-8). The story of the dissemination of rice cultivation is not yet clear but rice is known to occur in the context of the Indus tradition in Panjab and Haryana. The spread of different cultivated crops all over the subcontinent has its own story but roughly between the 8th and the 3rd millennia BC, most of the crops that we find in this region now attained more or less a subcontinental spread.

The ease with which many of the cultural traits spread from one part of the subcontinent to another had a lot to do with a basic character of its geography:

> The one clear unity which India possessed throughout history has been geographical. In no other part of the world, unless perhaps in South America, are the physical features on a grander scale. Yet no where else are they more simply combined into a single region.

This was written by a geographer, H.J. Mackinder (1922). To the south of the highlands from the western rim of Baluchistan to the Patkoi and Arakan Yoma in the east, there was no major hindrance to human movements from one part of the subcontinent to another. And yet, some later geographers ignored this element and tried to impose some arbitrary cultural divides and rigid lines of movements on its map. I have tried to discuss some of the relevant issues in my *The Geo-Political Orbits of Ancient India* (Chakrabarti 2010a). In trying to understand how different parts of the Indian subcontinent interacted throughout ancient history, the book underlines how politics was enacted in various geographical orbits that kept interacting throughout the period without any fixed boundary or 'divide'. By closely examining the focal geographical points along which ancient Indian dynasties tried to expand their political power and interact with other contemporary dynasties, the book highlights the range of geographical possibilities of the regional power centres of various periods in ancient India. It also underlines the extent to which they operated within that frame. The book further argues that the web of inter-regional interaction was not limited to a particular set of regions but had a pan-Indian ramification. None of the regions could therefore thrive in political isolation. It underscores that regions in ancient Indian history never had any immutable historical shape or identity but were fluid, both in their interactions and outlines.

The notion of fixed geographical lines has seriously harmed the cause of Indian archaeological studies. For instance, the date of anything with Gangetic origin in the Deccan has been put at least 200 years later than its date in its centre of origin in the Ganga Plain. The way the NBP, a distinctive Ganga plain pottery of c. 800 BC and later, has been dated in the Deccan is a case in point. In the Deccan the NBP has seldom been put before 300 BC. This has been very unwise because this has distorted the chronology of many Deccanese and even south Indian archaeological sites where cross-dating with the NBP is an important chronological marker. For instance, at Korkai, a port site in the Tamraparni delta area of the present-day Ramanathapuram district, a single radiocarbon date associated with its NBP-bearing level is in the 8th century BC or somewhat earlier. This was considered chronologically misfit, but a close examination of the NBP found in a neighbouring site, Alagunkalam, makes us feel that the Korkai date may well be correct because the Alagankulam material is identical in its colour and hue with the best Ganga Plain material (for a discussion of the issue, Chakrabarti 2010b). This is also likely to fit in the context of the radiocarbon date from a level at Porunthal near Palni at the foot of the Western Ghats in Tamil Nadu. This level contains sherds with Tamil-Brahmi inscriptions and the date has been found to be around 500 BC (490 +/- 30 BC, uncalibrated), showing that the beginning of the historical period in Tamil Nadu may well be roughly contemporary with that in the Ganga Plain (personal information from K. Rajan, 2011). The sheer quality of the few pieces of the NBP that occur at Alagankulam (examined by R. Tewari, R.N. Singh and myself in 2005) makes us wonder if these sherds cannot be as early as *c.* 800 BC. If so, there should not be much difficulty in describing the early historic growth in Tamil Nadu as a process that took place between *c.* 800 BC and *c.* 500 BC, something that took place in the Ganga plain too. Whatever may transpire in future, I find no reason why artifacts like the NBP should be invariably dated outside their original distribution zone some centuries later than the date of their origin in the Ganga Valley. There was much faster movement of cultural items all over the subcontinent than we are prepared to admit.

The openness of Indian physical geography except at its northern perimeter has facilitated the development of a dense network of routes linking its various parts. The literary sources may underline some of them but for the details archaeological groundwork is necessary. For the past two decades or so, I have been doing precisely this and may put forward some of the relevant conclusions in the rest of this paper.

The incorporation of the Uttarakhand Himalayas in the orbit of India's sacred geography is a fact acknowledged widely in the traditional literary sources. One wonders if archaeology can throw any light on the general range of chronology by which it was likely to have been achieved (discussed in detail in Chakrabarti 2007). This sector of the Himalayas has a few major entry-points from the plains. The first one is at Kalsi where the upper course of the Yamuna has carved an access route, the earliest antiquity of which is marked by the Asokan edict at Kalsi itself. This entry leads to the uppermost stretch of the Yamuna Valley where Purola is located. This is a Painted Grey Ware site. The second entry is at Haridwar, and here, not far from Haridwar itself and towards Hrishikesh, is a Painted Grey Ware site. From Hrishikesh the road to Badrinath passes through Srinagar which is about half-way towards Badrinath. Srinagar in its immediate vicinity has a Painted Grey Ware site. It may be added that the plain opposite Manasa Devi hill at Haridwar has yielded painted pottery of the Harappan tradition, and there are sites of the Ochre Coloured Pottery and painted pottery of the Harappan tradition in the Saharanpur plain at the foot of the range where Kalsi is located. The third entry is through Kotdwar near Najibabad. A route links Kotdwar with Pauri, from where it is possible to join the Hrishikesh-Badrinath route via Srinagar. The Najibabad sector also possesses Painted Grey Ware. The fourth entry is through

Kashipur which is easily accessible from Rampur. There is a rich Painted Grey Ware site near Kashipur and there are also sites with the painted pottery of the Harappan tradition in this area. The fifth major entry is from Tanakpur which takes one to Champawat and Pithoragarh sectors of Uttarakhand. There is a Buddhist stupa site of *c.* 2nd century BC a few kilometres west of Tanakpur but from somewhere in Pithoragarh copper anthropomorphs, which are considered inseparable parts of the upper Gangetic Valley 'Copper Hoards' and have to be considered related to the late Harappan tradition after the discoveries at Sinoli, have been reported. It may be noted that Pithoragarh lies on the way to Mansarovar.

It may be recalled that the Uttarakhand Himalayas are full of steep V-shaped valleys with little cultivable lands being available either at the valley-bottoms or on their sides. Why the Painted Grey Ware settlers were moving into this area along defined routes to some pilgrim centres ? Was there any awareness of this zone among the people of the Copper Hoard/late Harappan tradition in the plains at its gate ? Nobody present in this sector of the plain could be unaware of the hills but whether they decided to enter this or not is a different matter. There is as yet no valid archaeological evidence except the occurrence of copper anthropomorphs in Pithoragarh. As far as the Painted Grey Ware is concerned, the evidence is unequivocal: from the Uttarkashi sector (cf. Purola) to Haridwar entry and Srinagar the Painted Grey Ware people moved deep into the Uttarakhand Himalayas which loom large in the Indian sacred geography. There is no independent date of the Painted Grey Ware from this sector but a date around 1000 BC may broadly be accepted, providing a clue to the time when the sacred character of the geography of this part of the Himalayas may be assumed to have developed a clear profile. It is profiles such as these which throw light on how the cultural unity emerged at various points in various parts of the subcontinent.

Those familiar with the early political history of the subcontinent will know about the links of the Taxila region with the upper Ganga Plain. The importance of Takshasila near modern Rawalpindi in the early Indian literature is an important indicator of this link. No Indus site has yet been found in the Taxila area, but otherwise the entire area from Pakistani Panjab to the upper Ganga Plain is dotted with Indus sites, and our understanding is that this link between western Panjab and the upper Ganga Plain was maintained by two main alignments. The first one was Ludhiana-Ferozepur alignment which led to the Lahore sector, where Sohdara marked the ancient Chenab crossing. There is a straight run from Sohdara to Taxila with sites like Jhelam and Manikyala on the way. The second—and more important—alignment lay through Gurdaspur and Kalanour, both on the Indian side of the border. Kalanour is a massive site near the border and directly connected with Sialkot, from where Sohdara and thus the route to Taxila are easily approachable. What has to be understood that the linkage of the Taxila territory with the upper Ganga Plain near Delhi is rooted in the Indus times and takes textual shape by the time of the early Buddhist literature. Indus sites have not yet been found in the Sialkot sector of Pakistan and possibly not in the Lahore sector either. However, there are sites with pottery of the Indus tradition right up to the Siwaliks on the Indian side of Panjab and similarly there should be Indus-related sites up to the Siwaliks on the Pakistani side too (for the details, Chakrabarti 2010c). This is another instance of the subcontinent's cultural unity being given a chronological frame over a certain region.

These chronological frames will vary between different segments of the land. For instance, this chronological frame is considerably later in the case of the Bengal delta and the Brahmaputra Valley. The archaeological situations in both these areas are interesting. The available date of the NBP in the eastern part of the Bengal delta is *c.* 450 BC and there is no geographical difficulty in maintaining communications between this area and Assam along the Brahmaputra. In another part of the Bengal Delta the main communication point with Assam was the Karatoya Valley where a major archaeological site is located. This site—Mahasthangarh—has also yielded the NBP, although one is not sure of its radiocarbon dates here. The problem is that there does not seem to be any well-defined pre-NBP deposit in the Bangladesh part of the Bengal delta. This must be due to the lack of suitable work because Bangarh, only a short distance away from Mahasthangarh and in the same type of geographical setting, has recently yielded a substantial pre-NBP black-and-red ware deposit. The problem is more accentuated in the Assam section of the Brahmaputra Valley. No indisputable pre-Christian material has yet been found in this area. I can think of only two pieces of evidence: a second century BC bowl with incurved rim from the surface at Tejpur and a terracotta ring-well of about the same general period excavated in the cliff section of the Brahmaputra at the same place (information from S. Jamal Hasan 2011). I would argue that the Brahmaputra Valley part of Assam came into the Gangetic orbit by the beginning of the early historic period, although more positive data will be needed on this point.

The way the different sections of the subcontinent have interacted and shared elements of material culture calls for detailed research on the ground. The building up of its chronology segment by segment is also an important point. However, let there be no doubt about the closeness of this interaction in the material domain of life. One season I scraped some pottery of *c.* 200 BC out of a cliff at Ror in the hilly region of Kangra, part of the ancient Trigarta. Next season, I scraped the identical pottery out of the Damodar cliff at Pokharna in Bankura. The point is that by *c.* 200 BC there was hardly any noticeable difference between the pottery types of the entire sweep of the country from Kangra to Paschim Banga. The fact that this uniformity extends well back in time is beyond doubt, but detailed comparative studies between different areas still remain to be undertaken.

The Vindhya-Satpura divide is supposedly a major divide in Indian history and geography. Contrary to this impression, the Ganga Plain and the Deccan were linked by a host of routes, the antiquity of which can securely be placed in the mid-second millennium BC, if not considerably earlier. These routes had their own ramifications in the Deccan and the southern peninsula and carved out a vast unit of political and economic interaction between the Konkan coast and the Godavari delta on the one hand and between the area south of the Narmada and the furthest parts of Tamil Nadu and Kerala on the other. In 1999-2006 I studied these routes on the ground (Chakrabarti 2005, 2010b) beginning with the Gangetic Valley links with Maharashtra and Andhra. I shall offer a minimal outline of these routes in the rest of this paper.

Beginning with Rajagriha and Pataliputra, we find that the alignments towards the Deccan from these places converged upon Bhabua near Sasaram to follow the Bhabua to Chakia and Ahraura alignment towards Banaras which could be approached from this alignment in two ways: either from Ahraura or from Bhuili, the latter accessible directly from Chakia. The Ganga for Banaras was crossed at Ramnagar. From Ahraura a route went up to Mirzapur but a route also went across the Sonabhadra or Robertsganj Plateau to the crossing of the Son at Agori Khas, from where there were routes to the Ramgarh area in the southern section of Sarguja Plain. The Hasdo River was followed in this section to enter the Bilaspur section of Chhattisgarh and end up near Raipur. The options at Raipur were to travel to the Vizianagram section of the Andhra coast through Bastar or to travel straight to the modern Gondia section of Vidarbha to turn south towards the Karimabad-Nizamabad section of Andhra. One could also travel straight west till the Aurangabad section and eventually Paithan on the Godavari were reached.

The route which went from Ahraura to Mirzapur was joined at Mirzapur by a route which came from Banaras following the left bank of the Ganga till Agiabir where the Ganga was crossed for Mirzapur. This route was also joined by a route which came from Sravasti north of Ayodhya and passed through Jaunpur. From Mirzapur the route climbed the Vindhyan scarp near Lalganj and Halia and proceeded towards Rewa, the ancient Chedi country. The Rewa Plateau received the Deccan-bound routes also from ancient Prayag and Kausambi, which ascended the Vindhyas at Baldaha Ghat and Sohagi Ghat. A little beyond Rewa the route bifurcated, one going to Chhattisgarh through Bandhavgarh to join the Bilaspur-Raipur alignment. Another route went to Jabalpur and turned south emerging in the Banganga plain near Pauni through Balaghat. From Pauni, the northern section of Andhra was easily accessible. Or, the route moved from Jabalpur to the area south of Bhopal where the Narmada was crossed near Hosangabad and the Tapti at Burhanpur. Maharashtra was reached by crossing the Tapti at Burhanpur and passing by Asirgarh on the way.

Proceeding further north from Allahabad-Kausambi, one reaches the Kanpur area where a route comes through Lucknow, crosses the Ganga at Kanpur and goes up to Ghatampur on the bank of the Yamuna only to cross it and follow the Betwa River alignment up to Vidisha and beyond to reach the Narmada and finally Burhanpur. The Betwa alignment was joined by a route which came from the area of modern Etahwa.

Further up is the Agra-Mathura area. Here the initial target was to reach the Ujjain section of Malwa. Bateshwar on the Agra side was a major point and from here the line went straight to modern Shivpuri via Pawayya or ancient Padmavati, and from Shivpuri, the Ujjain area was approachable. The more important place in this section was Mathura. Here a part of Rajasthan had to be crossed to reach Malwa. Rajasthan was entered through Bharatpur and Deeg and the route went by Rupbas, Bayana and Ranthambhor till the Kota area and Ujjain beyond it were reached. My idea of this section is incomplete because I have just begun fieldwork (2011) in this sector. The importance of Ujjain is highlighted more if we think of an alignment moving from the direction of Delhi and Mathura towards the Malwa Plain, especially Mandasore from where Ujjain is only but a step. Mandasore is easily accessed from the Mewar Plain. From Ujjain there is a straight route through Nagda to Gujarat, but from Ujjain one can also cross the Narmada at Maheswar and follow the Kasargad-Burhanpur (Tapti crossing)-Ajanta-Bhokardan-Paithan alignment. From Ujjain one can also move towards Dhar and then go up to Barwani where also the Narmada can be crossed. From Barwani, the alignment beyond the Narmada is Dhulia-Chalisgaon-Pitalkhora-Ellora-Bhokardan (?) –Paithan. From Dhulia one can also go to Nasik, Kalyan or Sopara, the last two on the Konkan coast. From Nasik one can even go to Junnar and reach the Konkan coast through Malsejghat and Nanaghat.

In the next stage I tried to determine the major alignments within Maharashtra, Andhra and the southern regions up to Cape Comorin and Kerala. A major focus of this study was also the coastline from Daman on the Konkan coast to Srikakulam in the Vamsadhara estuary of Andhra which was home to almost innumerable pre-industrial ports, some of which played a major role in the ancient context too. In the Konkan coast our points of consideration were its geographical features, the distribution of its port sites and the links of communication between these ports and their Maharashtra and Karnataka hinterlands through a large number of passes in the Western Ghats. On the eastern side of the Western Ghats, the north- south alignment of Satara, Kolhapur and Belgaum plays a crucial role in mediating the routes which linked the different sections of the Konkan coast to a vast region covering large sections of inner Maharashtra, the Gulbarga-Bijapur-Badamy-Bellary section of Karnataka, and through them Andhra, and at a further remove, Tamil Nadu. One can also add to this network Solapur in the east and Dharwar in the south. Viewed in the context of such wider links, the narrow coastal plain of Konkan and the associated openings of varying importance in the Western Ghats cease to be a closed world and become an integral part of the vast network of routes covering the Deccan and the southern peninsula

In the case of Tamil Nadu and Kerala the situation is different and has been so mainly because of their different geographical characters. First, because of the presence of the Palghat gap, Tamil Nadu and Kerala have been closely linked historically. There are also some less prominent but nonetheless important openings to the south of the Palghat opening. Apart from the Palghat gap, all the passes linked to the Kerala coast led either to the Mysore Plateau or to the southern section of Tamil Nadu. In Tamil Nadu there are clear entry points in the north, which are linked to the Mysore Plateau and the Rayalseema tract of Andhra. These entry points are important to judge the flow of events in Tamil Nadu history. There are also uplands in the interior of Tamil Nadu. The configuration of these uplands and the Palghat gap have greatly influenced its internal lines of movements. Two communication lines have always been important: the Coimbature-Salem-Dharmapuri axis, with its own approach to the Kerala coast, and the axis from Kanchipuram-Madras sector to the areas down south up to Madurai and Tinnevelly.

The major internal barrier in Andhra lies in the Rayalseema sector where both across the Nallamalai and Erramala there are a few passes. These passes kept the line of communication between the Raichur Doab and Bellary sections of Karnataka and the Andhra coast between the mouth of the Krishna and Nellore open. Equally important is the opening of Tirupati, a camping ground of pilgrims from the north to Tirupati and further south. From Vidarbha and eastern India Andhra was open both on the north and the east.

Thus, right from the Ganga-Yamuna alignment to the southern tip of the peninsula there was a dense network of ancient routes giving material expression to the interconnection between different areas and the growth of a shared culture. By the middle of the second millennium BC most parts of the subcontinent were likely to be in the know of each other.

REFERENCES

Chakrabarti, D.K. and Nayanjot Lahiri. 1996. *Copper and Its Alloys in Ancient India.* Delhi: Munshiram Manoharlal.

Chakrabarti, D.K. 2005. *The Archaeology of the Deccan Routes.* Delhi: Munshiram Manoharlal.

Chakrabarti, D.K. 2007. *Archaeological Geography of the Ganga Plain: the Upper Ganga.* Delhi: Munshiram Manoharlal

Chakrabarti, D.K. 2010a. *The Geo-Political Orbits of Ancient India.* Delhi: Oxford University Press.

Chakrabarti, D.K. 2010b. *The Ancient Routes of the Deccan and the Southern Peninsula.* Delhi: Aryan Books.

Chakrabarti, D.K. 2010c. Notes on the Historical Geography of the Pakistani Panjab. *Pakistan Heritage* 2, pp. 79-85.

Pokharia, A.K. 2008. Palaeoethnobotanical Record of Cultivated Crops and Associated Weeds and Wild Taxa from Neolithic Site Tokwa, Uttar Pradesh, India. *Current Science* 94 (2): 248-55.

Pokharia, A.K., J.N. Pal, and Alka Srivastava. 2009. Plant Macro-Remains from Neolithic Jhusi in Ganga Plain: Evidence for Grain-based Agriculture. *Current Science* 97(4): 564-72.

Sali, S.A. 1986. *Daimabad.* Delhi: Archaeological Survey of India.

Sharma, D.V., K.C. Nauriyal, and V.N. Prabhakar. 2005-06. Excavations at Sanauli 2005-06: A Harappan Necropolis in the Upper Ganga-Yamuna Doab. *Puratattva* 36: 166-79.

Tewari, R., R.K. Srivastava, K.S. Saraswat, I.B. Singh and K.K. Singh. 2007-08. Early Farming at Lohuradewa. *Pragdhara, Journal of the U.P. State Archaeological Department* 18: 347-73.

10

Climate in the Indus Studies

Comments on L. GIOSAN et al. (2012)

Fluvial Landscapes of the Harappan Civilization, in *Proceedings of the National Academy of Sciences of the United States of America*, Environmental Sciences

I. GENERAL RESEARCH BACKGROUND

The *PNAS* paper by L. Giosan et al. in May 2012 is not the first attempt to link the fate of the Indus Civilization with climate, nor is the issue of aridity during this period discussed for the first time. On the basis of the Indo-French fieldwork in Haryana in 1983-84, M-A Courty (1987) argued that aeolian activity was contemporary with the proto-historical period and also anterior to it. Around Hissar she noted that "the protohistoric settlements lay on the loamy sandy plain already wind-eroded". The study of the sediment profile of the Lunkaransar lake bed in west Rajasthan led Y. Enzell et al. (1999, reprint in Lahiri 2000: 226-238) to conclude the following:

> The lake levels were very shallow and fluctuated often in the Early Holocene and then rose abruptly around 6300 BP. The lake completely desiccated around 4800 years BP. The end of this 1500-years wet period coincided with a period

> of intense dune stabilization. The major Harappan/Indus civilization began and flourished in this region 1000 years after desiccation of the lake during arid climate and was not synchronous with the lacustral phase...
>
> ... *The Indus civilization flourished mainly along rivers during times when northwestern India experienced semiarid climatic conditions that are similar to those at present.*"

In 2003 M. Staubwasser et al. (2003) observed the following:

> Planktonic oxygen isotope ratios off the Indus delta reveal climate changes with a multi-centennial pacing during the last 6 ka, with the most prominent change recorded at 4.2 ka BP. Opposing isotopic trends across the northern Arabian Sea surface at that time indicate a reduction in Indus river discharge and suggest that later cycles also reflect variations in total annual rainfall over south Asia. The 4.2 ka event is coherent with the termination of urban Harappan civilization in the Indus valley. Thus, drought may have initiated southeastward habitat tracking within the Harappan cultural domain. The late Holocene drought cycles following the 4.2 ka BP event vary between 200 and 800 years and are coherent with the evolution of cosmogenic 14C production rates. This suggests that solar variability is one fundamental cause behind Holocene rainfall changes over south Asia.

A more recent opinion is that of A.K. Gupta, M. Das and D.M. Anderson (2005):

> Our record shows that the summer monsoon, in general, was strongest in early Holocene marked by high amplitude shifts between dry and wet phases. The summer monsoon shows a gradual weakening over the past 8 kyr with more or less a stable dry phase beginning

> ~5 kyr BP that coincides with the onset of an arid phase in India and termination of the Indus valley civilization.

Earlier, A.K. Gupta (2004) tried to relate the origin of agriculture and domestication of plants and animals to early Holocene climatic amelioration (Gupta 2004). In 2006 A.K. Gupta et al. (2006) were more explicit in the Indus context:

> The increased aridity since ~ 5000 cal yrs BP influenced population and agricultural production in the Indus region. A gross decline in rainfall in the northwest and failure of agriculture necessitated adaptations and migrations of people to the east towards Ganga plain.

The *PNAS* paper is in the above research tradition. The basic contention of the paper is the following:

—— aridification intensified in the Harappan territory after *c.* 5000 BP (*c.* 3000 BC);

—— the river flows slowed down, leading to gradually decreased flood intensity

—— the gradual decrease in flood intensity led to intensive agriculture, leading in turn to urbanisation

—— there was a further decline in monsoon precipitation, leading to the weakening of the rivers dependent on the monsoon rains, increasing "the vulnerability of agricultural production supporting Harappan urbanism, leading to settlement downsizing, diversification of crops, and a drastic increase in settlements in the moister monsoon regions of the upper Panjab, Haryana and Uttar Pradesh.

II. COMMENTS

I am not qualified to comment on the scientific aspects of the research which has resulted in this publication. However, it is easily noted that this premise of a more or less continuous aridity—with more intensification after some time—more or less tallies with the premises of Courty, Enzell and Gupta. The point to note further is that archaeologically it is tied to a cascade of inferences, and that in the *PNAS* paper these inferences have been accepted as facts or something closely approximating facts. Here I propose to dwell only on some of them and argue *that academic conclusions based on them may be way apart from the science which has gone into the making of this paper.* Secondly, I shall argue that *the basically semi-arid/arid settings which have been invoked for the Harappan setting by the PNAS paper gets an indirect measure of support from some locations of sites and a study of some Haryana district gazetteers which depict the state of pre-modern agriculture of the region.* I believe that Enzell et al. 's opinion that during the period of the Indus Civilization "north-western India experienced semiarid climatic conditions similar to those at present" deserves serious consideration.

The major archaeological premises are three in number. The starting premise is that the early phase of the Harappan cultural tradition is rooted in the "antecedent agricultural communities of the hills bordering the Indus alluvial plain to the west". This premise negates any kind of influence from the east in the early Harappan phase and can be questioned on two counts. First, there has been evidence of rice in the early Harappan level of Kunal and Balu in Haryana for a long time. The identification of rice in these levels at these sites was done by K.S. Saraswat, and its implication from the point of view of an underlying rice-cultivating tradition was pointed out by me in 1999 (Chakrabarti 1999). The possibility of rice being an important item in the Harappan make-up was in fact suggested by me in 1989 (Chakrabarti 1989).One gathers that rice has recently been identified at another Haryana site called Masudpur (personal information from Dr. R.N. Singh)), which, in view of the earlier finds in Haryana, is hardly a surprise. If one simply remembers that rice cultivation in Haryana could only be an eastern derivation, as the earliest centre of rice cultivation in India has now firmly been identified at Lohuradeva in the trans-Sarayu plain, one has to admit that the Harappan cultural tradition cannot be something wholly rooted, as the authors of the *PNAS* article put it, in "the hills bordering the Indus alluvial plain to the west."

This inference gets strengthened when one remembers that the Aravalli alignment from the northeast to the southeast was an independent centre of food production in India. This inference was put forward by me in 2006 (Chakrabarti 2006) on the basis of a number of facts regarding the excavations at Bagor, Ganeshwar and Gilund in the Aravallis in Rajasthan. Regarding Ganeshwar it was pointed out that the copper metallurgy of Period II of the site was unlikely to have sprung straight from the microlith-using level of Period I unless Period I had an associated element of food production. Secondly, the fact that Bagor Period II and Ganeshwar Period II were closely related is shown by the identical character of the three copper arrowheads found in Bagor II and those found in Ganeshwar. A sixth-millennium BC 'mesolithic' stage was also isolated at Gilund. In the second edition of my *India: An Archaeological History* (2009) I argued that the conclusion that the Aravallis constituted an early and independent agricultural and metallurgical zone was getting inescapable.

My long-standing argument that the Aravallis marked a separate and independent zone of food production has recently been proved by the evidence of use-wear and starched –grain analysis of the microliths from both the aceramic and ceramic phases of Bagor

(Shinde 2008). This shows the use of a root-crop like ginger and other plants like sesame, horse-gram, date-palm and mango in the aceramic phase (5700–4500 BC) and the further use of tamarind, pigeon-pea, barley, ragi millet and jowar millet in the ceramic phase (4500–3500 BC). It cannot be accepted that this food production system in the 6th and 5th millennia BC in the Aravallis played no role in the formation of the early Harappan cultural tradition.

The second premise is that there was no system of canal irrigation in the Indus Civilization. I have not been able to trace the roots of this hypothesis, but one has to assume that this is just one of those things which, for reasons unknown, have been taken for granted. I argued first again this in 1995 (Chakrabarti 1995) in the context of Sind. Considering that the argument basically lay in something as important and as public as *The Imperial Gazetteer of India* (Vol. 23, 1908), published before the introduction of the modern irrigation system based on the Sukkur barrage in Sind, I was very surprised that nobody took this up before me. The *Gazetteer* points out that because the bed of the Indus is above that of the surrounding country, it creates "an easy means of irrigation, on which the agricultural prosperity of Sind entirely depends, by side channels drawn from the central river". It goes to emphasize the importance of irrigation in the agricultural life of the province:

> The dry character of the soil and the almost absence of rain render irrigation a matter of prime importance. Sometimes, indeed, for two or three years in succession, no rain whatever falls in the province. Under these circumstances *the Indus is to Sind what the Nile is to Egypt. When the province was annexed in 1843, numerous irrigation canals existed which derived their supply direct*

> *from the river* (italics added). These canals are carried away from the river bank in the direction the water can most easily flow to reach the fields that are to be irrigated. None of them has its head where the bank is really permanent, and they can draw off water only during the inundation season. The river must consequently rise several feet before the canal will fill. Many of these canals are but old deltaic channels, reopened and extended, and all have the appearance of rivers rather than artificial cuts.

Basically this situation prevailed in the nineteenth century and possibly in early parts of the twentieth. We have no way of arguing that this indeed was the situation during the Indus times, but considering that the pre-modern agricultural system is unlikely to have significantly changed since its beginning, it would be logical to infer that the agriculture of the Indus civilization, especially in Sind, was based on a canal irrigation system just as the ancient Egyptian and Mesopotamian agricultures were.

Subsequently, I tried to strengthen this premise by pointing out, on the basis of a doctoral dissertation, that at the turn of the twentieth century, a significantly greater percentage of agriculture in Sind was based on the canal irrigation system (Chakrabarti 1999).

In the case of Haryana, H. Francfort in his essay in *Eastern Anthropologist* (1992) wrote that it was "a small-scale system, less impressive than the great hydraulic works of Mesopotamia or Central Asia during the same period. But here, as well as there, the spatial unit is the network, or the branch, or the cluster of networks which mark the ground and define the irrigable areas for farming."

In Haryana irrigation works were a major historical feature. The wealth of the country, better known as the land of the Yaudheyas, was described in a text of *c.* 10th century AD:

> The Yaudheya country was like an ornament of the earth, and was replete with all requisites of good and happy life.... Its villages were full of cattle wealth, cows, buffaloes, goats, sheep, camels and horses. *Abundance of irrigation works rendered them free from the vagaries of Rains* (italics added). Their well-watered fields of black soil ... were green with harvests and gardens. They yielded such bouncing harvests that the farmers were unable to beat the grain and stack them properly...

Their villages and settlements had no rocks, stones and thorns and bushes. Their ladies, beautiful and robust, laden with ornaments, and dressed in tight garments worked in farms and fields, and attracted travellers (Datta and Phadke 1985: 50-51).

The third premise that there was a dispersal of Harappan settlements to the east after the Sarasvati system began to dry up has also been with us for a long time, although with shaky grounds. First, there is now little doubt that around 2000 BC there was a substantial number of Harappan settlements right up to the Delhi-Ghaziabad-Meerat-Saharanpur-Haridwar section of western UP, the principal excavated sites of this region being Hulas and Alamgirpur. Two dates from Hulas, which have been listed as from early phase of the 'late Harappans', are 2000 BC and 2560 BC (both uncalibrated). The earliest date from the Alamgirpur column is 2200 BC (calibrated) but there is about a metre of undated deposit below, and the date of the Harappan beginning at Alamgirpur may well be around 2500 BC, on this basis.

Dr. R.N. Singh, the recent excavator of Alamgirpur, sends the following note on the date of Alamgirpur:

> There were three trenches at Alamgirpur from where samples have been taken for AMS dating. The date ranges from 2288 to 2000 BC (cal) in SC and YD2 trenches. Only one date obtained from ZB2 trench which ranges between 2136 to 1976 cal BC. This trench has more than four undated layers of 1.2 meters. Hence there is no doubt that the site can be dated back to 2500 BC.

Dr. Singh further adds that according to the studies of the soil profile around Alamgirpur, there has been no change in the environmental setting of the place since the protohistoric period.

Whatever it is, there is no reason to assume that the beginning of the Harappan cultural tradition far to the east coincided with a 'late dispersal' of the Harappans in that direction.

The impression that sites in the eastern segment of the Harappan distribution area are later than those of the other areas is created by the way the sites have been reported by their excavators/explorers in this sector. Sites have been assigned to 'early, 'mature' and 'late' almost exclusively on the basis of the surface scatter of sherds without considering the possibility that allocating surface pottery to specific sub-periods of a cultural phase purely on the basis of shapes and designs can be a dangerous game, because the so-called 'early' shapes and designs continue well into the later periods. One has to wait for a more systematic study of the Mature and Late Harappan phenomenon in Haryana, Panjab and Uttar Pradesh before rushing to conclusions about the eastward dispersal of the Harappans. The present data do not suggest that there was indeed such a dispersal.

The notion that the basic environmental context of the Harappans in Panjab, Haryana and Uttar Pradesh was not much dissimilar from what we observe today in this region is based, from our point of view, on two points. First, there can be no question of the Sarasvati system completely drying up till the modern period. H.G. Raverty's study of the mediaeval sources up to the 14th century AD makes sure of this point. A 10th century AD inscription from Pehoa mentions an eastern branch of the Sarasvati or Prachi Sarasvati. That there was an effective canal irrigation network in Haryana is clear from the textual reference regarding the prosperity of Haryana that I have cited earlier. The essence of the problem was stated clearly by us in 2009 (Chakrabarti and Saini 2009: 36-37):

> Archaeologists have a major task ahead. They have to look at the distribution of the settlements of the Harappan tradition in the light of the assumption that it functioned in a landscape which could be as arid as it is today. Assuming that the three Naiwals of Panjab and the Haryana rivers in their pristine state already ceased to be non-perennial, can we explain the present distribution of the Indus-related sites of this area on the basis of the postulate that, although non-perennial, these rivers or dried-up rivers, as the Naiwals were, could accumulate a lot of water during the monsoon and support a fairly dense network of settlements for a long time? The possibility of such a situation need not be denied offhand. One has only to consult the early district gazetteers of Haryana to realize that there were ferries across the Ghaggar in the nineteenth century, Sotha being one such ferry crossing points. The point is that a Harappan site has also been reported at Sotha/Sotar. Further, there is reference to an extensive irrigation network in the Hissar district basing itself on the river channels. There is really no reason why an irrigation network could not exist in the Harappan time. ....

That the aridity of a region need not be a hindrance to its good agricultural production can be underscored by the situation that could be observed around Kalibangan in the early 1960s. The early 20th century Survey of India 1 inch = 1 mile sheets showed only sand dunes in the area, but as the water of the Rajasthan Canal Project began to arrive in the dried Ghaggar-Sarasvati bed and as the farmers began to use this water for irrigation, the Ganganagar district began to attract attention as one of the richest districts of the country. The point is that the onset of aridity does not have to have any link with the development and decline of the Indus Civilization along the Ghaggar-Hakra system. Among other things, a good number of sites of this tradition are located on sand dunes in Haryana and Panjab.

In an article focussed not merely on the hard science of the climate studies but also on a densely scattered archaeological premises, there are always ample scopes to differ with the authors on various archaeological issues and their interpretations. In a sense this *PNAS* article has consolidated the process of concern with the climate of the Indus Civilization, and the idea that this civilization has to be appreciated in an environmental context the trace of which possibly still survives seems to be serious enough not to warrant off-hand dismissal.

Many authors of the *PNAS* study are not climate specialists in any sense. Their input was possibly in the field of archaeological hypotheses, and it is here that they stuck to many unverifiable assumptions. Sophisticated climate science and debatable archaeological assumptions of the archaeologists/archaeobotanists of the *PNAS* paper do not go well together.

REFERENCES

Chakrabarti, D.K. 1989. *Theoretical Issues in Indian Archaeology*. Delhi: Mumnshiram Manoharlal.

Chakrabarti, D.K. 1995. *The Archaeology of Ancient Indian Cities*. Delhi: Oxford University Press.

Chakrabarti, D.K. 1999. *India, an Archaeological History*. Delhi: Oxford University Press.

Chakrabarti, D.K. 2006. *The Oxford Companion to Indian Archaeology*. Delhi: Oxford University Press.

Chakrabarti, D.K. and Saini, S. 2009. *The Problem of the Sarasvati River and Notes on the Archaeological Geography of Haryana and East Panjab*. Delhi: Aryan Books.

Courty, M. 1987. 'Notes'. *Man and Environment* 11: 123-24.

Datta, V.N. and H.A. Phadke. 1985. *History of Kurukshetra*. Kurukshetra: Vishal Publications.

Gupta, A.K. 2004. Origin of Agriculture and Domestication of Plants and Animals Linked to Early Holocene Climatic Amelioration. *Current Science* 87: 54-59.

Gupta, A.K., D. Anderson, D.N. Pandey and A.K. Singhvi. 2006. Adaptation and Human Iimmigration, and Evidence of Agriculture Coincident with Changes in the Indian Summer Monsoon during the Holocene. *Current Science* 90: 1082-90.

Gupta, A.K., M. Das and D.M. Anderson. 2005. Solar Influence on the Indian Summer Monsoon during the Holocene. *Geophysical Research Letters*, 32, L17703.

Lahiri, N. (ed.). 2000. *The Decline of the Indus Civilization*. Delhi: Permanent Black Linked to Early Holocene Climatic Amelioration.

Shinde, V. 2008. Cultural Development from Mesolithic to Chalcolithic in the Mewar Region of Rajasthan, India. *Pragdhara* 18 201-13.

Staubwasser, M., et al. 2003. Climate Change at the 4.2 ka BP Termination of the Indus Valley Civilization and Holocene South Asian Monsoon Variability. *Geophysical Research Letters,* vol. 30, 1425 doi: 10.102.

11

Rethinking Early Mediaeval India, a Reader

UPINDER SINGH (ed.)

Delhi, 2011: Oxford University Press

If one decides to edit a volume on a particular theme, the editor accepts the responsibility of pointing out why the theme calls for a 'Reader' in the first place, and as far as the selection of sub-themes and the essays on them are concerned, the editor has to offer brief research narratives on each essay and has the added task of pointing out how the selected pieces fit in those research narratives. In her 'Reader' on 'early mediaeval' India Upinder Singh does none of these things.

She begins her introduction by accusing R.C. Majumdar of the folly of equating ancient India to Hinduism. One is not sure which religions there were in ancient India except Hinduism, Buddhism and Jainism, the last two being the offshoots of Hinduism itself.

On the nature of relationship between Hinduism and Buddhism on the historical level, I shall cite R.C. Dutt, *Civilization in Ancient India:*

> Buddhism had never assumed a hostile attitude towards the parent religion of India; and the fact that the two religions existed side by side for long centuries increased their toleration of each other. In every country Buddhists and orthodox Hindus lived side by side. Hindus went to Buddhist monasteries and Universities, and Buddhists learned from Brahmin sages. The same Kings favoured the followers of both religions. The Gupta Emperors were often worshippers of Shiva and Vishnu, but loaded Buddhists and Buddhist monasteries with gifts, presents and favours. One king was often a Buddhist and his son an orthodox Hindu; and often two brothers followed or favoured the two religions without fighting. Every Court had learned men belonging to both the religions, and Vikramaditya's Court was no exception to the rule.

Jainism was no different in relation to Hinduism. Throughout the length and breadth of the subcontinent, one finds sacred spots littered with images of all the religions of the time—Hindu, Buddhist and Jaina, with their iconographies liberally borrowing from each other.

From the first century AD onward we had also an element of Christianity along the southern coasts, but in an all-India perspective, it was a minor strain. The same may be said about the pre-conquest Islam in the west coast. Although the Rastrakutas had a Muslim governor and a king of the Gujarat area donated land for the setting up of a mosque and for its maintenance, the pre-Sultanate Islam played a negligible role in the subcontinent.

I have deliberately cited Ramesh Chandra Dutt above, because he wrote a book specifically equating ancient India to 'Hindu civilization': *Early Hindu Civilization* Calcutta, 1927.

However much Upinder Singh may dislike associating ancient Indian civilization with Hinduism, it will be difficult to get rid of the idea in Indian historiography.

In her introduction, Upinder Singh includes a panegyric of R.S. Sharma who is known principally for his work on the history of the Sudras in ancient India and for trying to evolving a theory of ancient Indian feudalism. According to Sharma, the feudal period of ancient India falls between *c.* AD 500 and *c.* AD 1200. In fact, it is roughly this period, i.e. *c.* AD 600–1200, which has been taken as the period of 'early feudalism' in this volume without explaining why 100 years have been taken off the beginning postulated by Sharma. In the introduction Singh also thanks D.D. Kosambi for turning our attention away from the ancient Indian political history to the understanding of its socio-political processes. The two volumes that Kosambi wrote on ancient Indian history contain many factual errors, and to argue that the study of the socio-economic history and processes in ancient India began or even received an impetus because of Kosambi's writings would be deviating from the historical truth.

I do not, however, get the impression that historical truth matters very much in Upinder Singh's quest. She is entitled to designate her period in any way she likes, but there is no special reason to argue that it is 'early mediaeval' unless one accepts wholesale R.S. Sharma's notion of 'feudalism' in India during that period. Even if we ignore the facts that land grants in favour of the Brahmins date from the period of the Buddhist *Jatakas* (*c.* 500 BC; U.N. Ghoshal, *The Agrarian System in Ancient India*, Calcutta 1930) and that numerically the land grant inscriptions constitute only a very small percentage of the total number of inscriptions of the relevant dynasties, absolutely no consideration has been taken of the fact that in Europe itself 'feudalism' has been a very uncertain concept. As E. Brown pointed out long back ('The Tyranny of a Construct: Feudalism and Historians of Mediaeval Europe', *The American Historical Review* 79 (4), 1974, pp. 1063-88),

> Countless different, and sometimes contradictory definitions of the terms exist, and any and all these definitions are hedged around with qualifications. Using the terms seems to lead almost invariably to treating the ism or its system as a sentient, autonomous agent.

If one is not constrained to work within the circle of any such 'ism', one would say that the increased number of land grant inscriptions suggests nothing more than agricultural expansion. I pointed out this in *Theoretical Issues in Indian Archaeology* (Delhi 1988), and I find no reason yet to change my position. This agricultural growth led to a significant growth of secondary states in various areas, states which emerged with all the trappings of an ancient Indian state. The way Sharma tried to strengthen his hypothesis by arguing an urban decay on the ground that the archaeological levels of the period had not enough burnt-brick structures or his idea that there was a serious decline of trade and coinage during that period would have been laughed off as a rather crude imitation of ideas in Henry Pirenne's *Mohammed and Charlemagne* but for the fact that as the chairman of the Indian Council of Historical Research his dictates and the dictates of his protégés ran unquestioned for a long time all over the land in matters of historical studies. Apparently, questioning of entrenched historical hypotheses offered by powerful people is not part of Upinder Singh's historical world.

Apart from Sharma's 'how feudal was Indian feudalism', this 'reader' consists of twelve articles, beginning with an essay by Burton Stein on the 'segmentary state'. Inquiring the structure of Chola state is a valid exercise but what do Indians learn from the premise that the state was modelled on how an African group called the Alurs ran their political business ? There is no answer to this and the other similar models discussed in many other essays of this volume. One may be allowed to infer that 'smart' writings in the field of 'early mediaeval' in Upinder Singh's dictionary have to show familiarity with sundry Western (read 'white') scholars (cf. John Leavitt whose writing has been remembered by Kunal Chakrabarti even while writing on something as Bengali as *Mangalkavyas* and *Mangalchandis*). The praise showered by Upinder Singh herself on Sinopoli and Morrison for their 'in-depth' archaeological study of the Vijayanagara state will not be shared by many Indian archaeologists. Let me add as an aside that my review of an archaeological report by these two authors was rejected by the American journal *Journal of Field Archaeology* which sent the volume to me for review in the first place. I suppose I could not be adulatory enough to the learned authors. There are, of course, some honest-to-goodness articles in this volume. Tamil Nadu *Nagaram*, the Kakatiya period Andhra, dancing *Kinnaras*—these all have been dealt with in a matter-of-fact way which people can follow and understand. Kulke's idea of early mediaeval state formation in 'three concentrically connected geographical areas' is worth examining in detail on the basis of maps and concrete inscriptional data. But considering Upinder Singh's predilection for archaeological data, i.e. the material remains of life, one finds it very surprising that the volume contains nothing at all on agriculture, settlements, technology and trade of the period. Will this mean that there is hardly any research done in these fields in the context of a very large segment of Indian history (*c.* AD 600–1200)?

I regret that I have turned out a disappointing review of a volume edited by somebody whom I recollect as a bright young history student of Delhi University about thirty years ago. Regrettably, the Indian historical world, even the section dealing with ancient India, is very coterie-driven and prefers to put on a garb of great intellectualism. It is very much under the tyranny of constructs. It is also very political, tied in various ways to the deities of the Indian Establishment in the fields of history, politics and even other areas. It is an unpleasant world, and the present Oxford University Press volume is a sharp reminder of this unpleasantness. Throughout its 350-odd pages there is not even a whiff of smell of the land, the present landscape of which hides various layers of its 'early mediaeval' antecedence.

12

Inter-regional Interaction and Urbanism in the Ancient Indus Valley, a Geologic Provenience Study of Harappan Rock and Mineral Assemblage

R.W. LAW

Kyoto 2011: Research Institute for Humanities and Nature. Occasional Paper 11, Linguistics, Archaeology and Human Past

This 800-page monograph, printed in excellent paper and with innumerable photographs, drawing, maps and appendices, cannot be said to be meant for most of the Indian, or even south Asian, archaeologists. I have had access to the occasional papers of this Kyoto institute before, but invariably because some privileged friends decided to lend their copies to me. I could not get them in Delhi bookshops or even in the libraries I know. I am forced to raise this point of availability of the First World books on Third World archaeology to the Third World archaeologists themselves because this is certainly one of the ways in which the First World archaeology tries to maintain its power over the Third World archaeological mind. How many of us have even seen the volumes published by the European Association of South Asian archaeologists? Knowledge is power, and quite cleverly, the First World archaeologists try to keep it restricted among a chosen few in the Third World. They will not dream of pulling down their own worth by publishing with a Delhi publisher, at least not unless they get a Western publisher first. I have been told to my face in a First World archaeological set-up that "Indian publications do not matter".

If I were not so disgusted by the racism implicit in the way the First World does archaeology in the Third World, I would have welcomed the publication of this volume, although I would have liked it less cluttered with non-essentials including sermons on the structure of the Indus civilization. To begin with, it would have done well without the load of its 'foreword' and 'preface' and the vast array of 'appendices' including the one on 'provenience vs. provenance'. The most charming aspect of the book is the infectious enthusiasm of its young writer for rocks and minerals in South Asia. He would not have been able to marshall the kind of evidence he has detailed unless he had thoroughly enjoyed himself doing it.

As far as the academic contents go, the outline is the following. It sets out to identify the source areas of some of the raw materials excavated by the American team at Harappa: grinding stones, cherts, steatite, agate, vesuvianite-grossular, alabaster, limestone, lead, silver and copper. The "strategies and methods for sourcing stone and metal artefacts" (chapter 3) meant using both primary geological references and information from the groups dealing with different kinds of stone for a living. The basic mineralogical testing involved X-ray diffraction analysis, electron microprobe analysis, spectrometric analysis and instrumental neutron activation. The mathematical tools which were used to infuse some sense in the data accumulated through the above-mentioned techniques were bivariate plotting and multivariate approaches involving canonical discriminant analysis and cluster analysis.

Not being a scientist, I cannot comment on the mineralogical testing or the mathematical tools, but can certainly follow the author's conclusions in the case of each raw material. The author himself is honest enough to admit that all the science-based inferences he makes regarding the geological sourcing of a stone or metal artefact "should always be considered as provisional". This is a great change from the days when any science-based composition analysis of an archaeological object had the impact of a biblical truth in our non-scientific mind.

Grinding stones (chapter 5) were of the following kinds: Delhi Quartzite which came from the Kaliana Hills of Haryana, grey sandstone which was collected as water-worn cobbles from the Siwalik foothills, Pab sandstone of the Sulaiman range and Baluchistan interior, and the sandstone of the Kirana Hills of Panjab. About one third of the grinding stone specimens remained unassociated with a specific rock-type. Whether the sources became more diversified in the mature period or not is always debatable.

The most common variety of chert (chapter 6) at Harappa is the black-brown chert of Sakesar limestone of the Salt range along with the black chert of the Great Limestone Formation of Jammu and the Moro Formation of the area of the Bolan Pass. Tan-Grey chert of the Rohri Hills also occurs extensively and the author detects an exclusive use of the Rohri Hills chert during the Mature Harappan phase at the site.

The relevant geological deposits of steatite (chapter 7) occur in Las Bela, Kalat, Zhob, Kurram Agency, Khyber Agency, Peshawar district, Mohmand Agency, Chitral, the northern areas of Gilgit and Hunza, Swat, Hazara, Jammu and Kashmir, Himachal Pradesh, Rajasthan and Gujarat. The conclusion is that the most important sources of steatite excavated at Harappa are the Dolomite sources of the northern areas of Pakistan and India.

The potential Harappan agate sources (chapter 8) include Gujarat (Ratanpura or southeastern Gujarat, northern Gujarat, Little Rann of Kutch, eastern Gujarat and Saurashtra), peninsular, central and eastern India, and the northern deposits north of the upper Indus Basin. After analysis Gujarat emerged as the principle agate source for the site of Harappa, although the better known Ratanpura deposits turned out to be less significant than the comparatively less known deposits in Kutch.

The chapter on vesuvianite-grossular (chapter 9) or a stone which was earlier mistaken to be jadeite, etc. and thus of Central Asiatic derivation, has shown this to be a kind of green stone which occurs widely but had its principal source for the Harappans in the Mohmand-Malakand regions and Baluchistan. The author further adds (p. 322) that " the only material in Harappa's rock and mineral assemblage from which drills capable of perforating vesuvianite-grossular could have been fashioned was Ernestite" which also came principally from the vesuvianite-grossular-bearing areas.

In the chapter on alabaster (chapter 10) the author first distinguishes between selenite or gypsite of the gypsum beds of the Thar desert, western Sind and Gujarat and true alabaster of the Salt range, Sulaiman range, Kohat, and broadly the western Himalayas. The alabaster sources for Harappa are less defined but could include the Salt range, the Sulaiman range and even the western Himalayas. An interesting feature is the isolation of 'Mari diamonds' or small pink-coloured quartz crystals at Harappa, which probably came with the Salt range alabaster.

The chapter on limestone (chapter 11) is particularly intriguing because of the range of artefacts it displays. Of singular interest is the mould terracotta tablets from Lakhanjodaro (p. 357) which apparently shows a pillar on the model of a palm tree surmounted by two stone rings topped by a T-shaped capital with both stylized human and plant designs. In two cases the pillars rise out of a circular and thick base, also with stylized designs. Limestone fragments possibly belonging to a sculpture, which were found in Pandit Dayaram Sahni's excavations and are now kept in the reserve collection of the Harappa museum are interesting too, although the reconstructions shown on p. 360 are purely arbitrary. The fragments may be part of a sculpture on the model of the limestone sculpture reported by F.R. Allchin from a London dealer's collection. There were multiple sources of limestone, some as far as Kutch and Jaisalmer. Whether large chunks of limestone were finding their way to Harappa from Jaisalmer is a debatable point.

The last relevant chapter (chapter 13) tries to source lead, silver and copper at Harappa. Lead supposedly came from Jammu and Kashmir, southern Baluchistan and an unidentified area. Southern Baluchistan seems to be a good source for argentiferous galena or silver although the source of silver in a ring from Gola Dhoro in Gujarat has been traced as far as Oman (p. 443). Raw copper ore is limited at Harappa and has been attributed to the "sources to the west of the Indus valley, or perhaps, Oman" (p. 460), not a particularly edifying or convincing hypothesis.

On the whole, this volume is less of a book and more of a reference manual meant for specialists in sourcing archaeological raw materials. This concern to locate the sources of raw materials found at archaeological sites is as old as the archaeological research itself. If I remember correctly, the occurrence of Rohri Hill chert was identified at Sutkagendor on the Makran Coast sometime in the nineteenth century, long before it was identified as a Harappan site. This book adequately underlines the complexity of the provenance studies, but it would certainly be foolhardy to accept any of its historical premise without careful scrutiny.

13

The Lost River, on the Trail of the Sarasvati

MICHEL DANINO

Delhi, 2010: Penguin Books

This book calls for careful reading. Its Part I, 'The Lost Sarasvati' is divided into three chapters : 'The Lost River of the Indian Desert', 'The mighty Sarasvati, and 'New Light on an Ancient River'. The first chapter discusses how the Sarasvati research was shaped in early years, beginning with Rennell and Tod. I thank the author for bringing in the work of Majors Colvin and Mackeson and for highlighting the role of the French historical geographer Vivien de Saint-Martin in identifying the river with the one of the Vedic tradition. Whether Robert Sivewright and his modern followers are correct in their belief that the Rann of Kutch is the delta of the Hakra is a different matter. It is possible that the Hakra flowed past Lakhpat at the western edge of the Rann, and as Lakhpat is an Indus site, the importance of the Hakra course via Lakhpat is obvious. The author seems to pull down slightly the importance of H.G. Raverty's account of the Ghaggar-Hakra drainage system from the Siwaliks to the sea. It was largely based on an unpublished survey report of the whole of the relevant region. The name of this surveyor was not mentioned, but from a reference in Alexander Cunningham's book on the ancient geography of India, I deduce that his name was Mirza Afzal Beg who was in the employ of Colonel Wilford. Raverty's account also takes into detailed consideration the whole lot of the relevant mediaeval Muslim textual sources. His description of the different sections of the Ghaggar-Hakra drainage leaves no doubt that the drainage system was alive, at least in many patches, well into the mediaeval period. Partly the same impression is achieved from a reading of the late nineteenth century district gazetteers of the Haryana area. I am slowly coming round to the belief that the Indus Civilization could have developed, flourished and declined in an environmental setting which, minus its population density and the consequent ecological damages, could not be far dissimilar from what is obtained in these areas today. I encountered a site of the Harappan tradition in Haryana, which was found after the landowner removed the sandy top soil. By digging through the deposit he also reached a similar deposit of sands.

The literary references to the Sarasvati form the content of the chapter two. The author cites various opinions but hesitates to categorically state that the people who argue against the identification of the Ghaggar-Hakra drainage lines with the Vedic Sarasvati belong in fact to the lunatic fringe of ancient Indian studies. It has been pointed out right in the opening page of *The Problem of the Sarasvati River and Notes on the Archaeological Geography of Haryana and Indian Panjab* that Edward Thomas' identification (1883) of the Helmand with the prototype of the Vedic Sarasvati had no logic behind it and that it was even ignored by his contemporaries. The evidence of the satellite imageries is discussed in the chapter 3, and if I have to opt for a particular discussion on this topic I shall opt for the discussion by Sharma, Gupta and Bhadra in *Puratattva,* 2005-2006. Regarding the idea that the Sutlej used to flow into the Hakra, I have found no answer to what was written in the *Calcutta Review*, Vol. 80, 1875, p. 323 : according to the Bahawalpur irrigation survey of 1869 , the bed of the Hakra in Bahawalpur was higher by 30 feet than the Sutlej bed and that there was no appearance in this locality, i.e. the Bahawalpur locality, of the characteristic alluvial deposit of the Panjab rivers (the comments cited in *The Problem, etc.*, p. 6). It appears that if one has to come to grips with what was actually there in the nineteenth century, an in-depth study of the various irrigation reports of the period throughout the region will be necessary. These may at least help in the interpretations of various satellite imagery maps.

Part II of the book, 'India's First Civilization', is divided into five chapters describing the basic features and associated problems of the study of the Indus Civilization. These are clearly written and argued chapters and I find them much better than the writings of the current bunch of Euro-American 'Indus specialists', many of whom have been mentioned by the author. Before making any comment on the movements of the Harappans, we must realize that the Harappan tradition extended in a vast zone from Panjab to western U.P. right up to the Siwaliks and that we still do not have any well-dated comparative stratigraphy over this region. There is no reason to believe *Prima facie* that the sites of western U.P. are later than those in the western parts of the Harappan distribution zone.

A major contribution of the author lies in Part III where in the four chapters including an epilogue, he discusses what he considers to be the tangible and intangible heritage of the Indus Civilization. The ratio of measurements which he traces at Dholavira and other sites including some historical and generally pre-modern sites seems to make positive sense in the light of the traditional measurement units of ancient India. It appears that slowly a new field of investigation is being opened and that the author seems to be particularly equipped to play a major role in this development. For what it is worth, I here draw attention to the terracotta representation of a wooden writing tablet from Mohenjo-daro, which B.B. Lal reproduces in one of his books. There is no doubt that this is the image of a wooden writing tablet, the like of which can be seen in the hands of thousands of students of Hindi-medium primary schools in many parts of northern India including Delhi. I regret that till I saw the illustration in Lal's book, I did not notice it, but the point is that this is almost a conclusive proof that literacy was far more widespread than we think in this civilization which apparently also ran a schooling system. There is an interesting section on the symbolism of horns in Danino's book, and it is interesting to reflect that now there are many terracotta representations of horns from a number of sites in the Haryana-Rajasthan belt. The evidence of fire-worship has also been marshalled with care.

The 'epilogue' summarises the basic problem and hypotheses regarding the Sarasvati. That there was a parallel river-system to the east of the Indus and that this river-system was mentioned in a solid chunk of the ancient Indian literature are important historic issues by themselves. That it was also one of the primary zones of the Indus Civilization gives the problem an unusual amount of significance. No purpose is served by mixing it with the Aryan problem. The present reviewer has argued in his *Colonial Indology: Sociopolitics of the Ancient Indian Past* (1997) that the Aryan idea is nothing but a racist myth and the sooner we come out of the stranglehold of this myth in the study of ancient India the better. To get an idea of this and many other related issues, Michel Danino's book deserves careful reading.

14

The Decline of Buddhism in India, a Fresh Perspective

K.T.S. SARAO

Delhi, 2012: Munshiram Manoharlal Publishers Pvt. Ltd.

This is a work of outstanding scholarship and calls for detailed discussion. A focussed survey of the state of Buddhism in various parts of India is followed by a critical examination of the different theories which have been proposed for the decline of Buddhism in the country and the author's own model for its decline.

Chapter 1 raises some crucial issues: can one give a continuous account of Buddhism's decline, especially when the data are either absent or of widely varying quality? Was the process of decline chronologically uniform or was it even consistent? The author's central point in this chapter is that by the time the Turks arrived in the heartland of Buddhism, this religion had totally lost its vigour and its decline was 'a fait accompli'. His account of the survival of Buddhism in post-12th century India is thorough. Somehow, he misses the fact (recorded in the *Bombay Gazetteers*) that there were some Buddhist monks even in the old Kanheri monastery of Mumbai. A full-fledged work on the phenomenon of post-12th century Buddhism in India is perhaps necessary, and that should include the Portuguese sources.

Chapter 2 offers the story of Buddhist decline in *Madhyadesa* (Bihar, Jharkhand, Uttar Pradesh, eastern Haryana, northern Madhya Pradesh, northern Chhattisgarh, northeastern Rajasthan and Nepalese *Terai*), Orissa, Bengal and Assam, Sind, Panjab and the northwest, Kashmir, western India and the adjacent region, and the Deccan. The accounts of the Chinese pilgrims, especially those of Xuangzang and Faxian, are a major historical source in this context. The chapter is full of many scholarly details, but I see no reason why Ramsharan Sharma's hypotheses of urban decay and trade decline, both crudely and illogically formulated, should come into the picture at all. The issue of 'moral and ethical degeneracy' discussed in Chapter 3 lists in detail the various behavioural lapses of the Buddhist community, but at the same time the author rightly points out that such behaviour was not universal. The element of Brahmanical animosity is dealt with in Chapter 4, and one is amused by the citation of G. Verardi's opinion that religious tolerance was unknown in pre-British India. Verardi is entitled to his opinion but the author argues that the persecution of Buddhism was never a serious or consistent feature of ancient Indian society. This reviewer believes that there may be some truth in the story of Pushyamitra Sunga's hostile feelings toward Buddhism. Archaeological evidence has emerged strongly at Deur Kothar near Rewa where the stupa complex was vandalised in the immediately post-Mauryan phase. The animosity supposedly displayed by Brahmanical-Hindu kings, of which the Pushyamitra example is one, has been discussed in Chapter 5. An interesting detail draws attention to the opinion of some French scholars that the Greek king Demetrius invaded India as a saviour of the Buddhists. Considered along with

Verardi's view that there was no religious tolerance in India in the pre-British period, views such as this unqualifiedly support the present reviewer's premise in *Colonial Indology* that it is one of the underlying aims of Western Indologists to depict India in a poor light. The Pushyamitra section is elaborate in this book and based on both archaeological and literary sources. The author's attitude to his sources is admirably critical. He refuses to accept that there was any substance in the Buddhist allegation against Pushyamitra Sunga. Regarding the later king Sasanka of Bengal, I would point out that the tradition of his persecution of the Buddhists is likely to be untrue because, having been involved in the excavations of the stupa of Raktamrittika Vihara in the outskirts of Sasanka's capital Karnasuvarna for many years, I would argue that there is absolutely no evidence of destruction in the structural history of this stupa site except in its latest levels dated 12th century AD and later. The author cites various scholarly opinions on the Sasanka issue and points out the pitfalls of this tradition popularised by Xuangzang who himself found Buddhism in a flourishing condition in Sasanka's kingdom. The author's comment in this context is very perceptive:

> The concept of a 'state religion' being foreign to the Indian mind, it would be unhistorical to assign any perceptible part of the decline to the withdrawal of patronage by rulers.

Chapter 6 is on 'sectarianism and the rise of Mahayana and Vajrayana'. It was only a simple step from Vajrayana to the Sahajiya and Tantric practices, resulting in a close integration of Buddhism with Hinduism. The author's knowledge of this process is remarkably broad-based, and I am delighted to find that he cites even Shashibhushan Dasgupta's *Obscure Religious Cults* to argue his case. As he states, "ritual eclectism made boundaries between Buddhists and Brahmanical-Hindus quite porous, if not altogether non-existent in some instances". His use of the iconographic sources of the period, especially of eastern India, is very knowledgeable, although, as far as I know, some scholars deny the presence of the Buddhist tradition in the Dharma Thakur cult of Bengal. In any case, the customs of Hindu and Buddhist Tantras "blended the two set-ups so comprehensively that the existence of Buddhism as a distinct entity became unfeasible".

Chapter 7 discusses the "attacks by Arabs and Turks" as a causative factor of the decline of Buddhism. In view of all the factors cited above, the advent of Islam cannot be the only, or even the main, factor in this context, but as Islam is generally intolerant of the infidels, some amount of Buddhist-bashing must have taken place as the Muslim armies swept up towards eastern India. It does not take much time to come across idols whose heads or noses have been detached by hitting them with an iron shovel. In the entire alluvial plain between the Bay of Bengal and the Siwaliks, precisely two semi-dilapidated brick temples of the Kalachuri period are still standing (near Naimish)– three, if one includes the Bhitargaon temple near the Yamuna beyond Kanpur. Major temples must have got destroyed in the first flush of the Islamic conquest of the Ganga plain. There is no point in trying to gloss over the issue. The Islamic conquest is an important feature of Indian history, and being a conquest, it must have had its rough sides too. I think that Haraprasad Sastri's opinion that the major Buddhist monasteries were put to sword and fire, which the author cites, must have an element of truth. The Raktamrittika Mahavihara near Karnasuvarna had its last phase in about this period.

Chapter 8 deals with the role of the Sufi saints in the Islamic scenario, which is followed by the revival of Brahmanical Hinduism and the rise of Bhakti movement in Chapter 9. Towards the end, in Chapters 10 and 11, the author offers a comprehensive analysis of the withering away of the primary force of Buddhism from India. It was basically due to the combination of a whole lot of factors outlined in the previous chapters.

It is a remarkably comprehensive research work on a very broad historical canvas. Almost at every step this reviewer has been impressed by the depth of the author's knowledge and unwavering focus on the historical details. This may turn out to be one of the most important publications of this period on ancient India.

15

Bhagwanlal Indraji, the First Indian Archaeologist: Multidisciplinary Approaches to the Study of the Past

VIRCHAND DHARAMSEY

Vadodara, 2012: Darshak Itihas Nidhi

This is a well-crafted, well-researched and a tastefully produced book. This is also highly motivated by the author's love to know about old archaeological discoveries in general and the central character of the book, Pandit Bhagwanlal Indraji, in particular. The book opens a new window on the history of archaeological research in western India.

People consulting the various volumes of the old Bombay district gazetteers must have been impressed by a superior level of historical and archaeological scholarship displayed there. Archaeological sections, especially those on the Buddhist rock-cut caves of western India and their inscriptions, were contributed by Bhagwanlal Indraji (a good Bengali, I prefer to write his name as Bhagavanlal Indraji !), and most of us have been familiar with his Sopara report. However, his range of scholarship and research roamed well beyond these concerns with western India. He was as rooted in pan-Indian Indological and archaeological scholarship as was his contemporary Rajendra Lal Mitra. The author has highlighted this aspect of Indraji's scholarship with loving care, and for that we are all very thankful to him. Interestingly, Mitra had a wide range of public activities besides his scholarly ones, and from this point of view, it is Indraji's patron, Bhau Daji, who reminds me of Mitra.

The section on Bhau Daji which has been discussed along with the fate of the Cave Temples Commission contains much new information. The role played by the various members of this Commission in the epigraphical discoveries and researches has been carefully listed by the author and will be the starting point of any future work on the history of the Commission.

It is after carefully introducing us to the general archaeological scene in Bombay that the author brings in Indraji, although his background in Junagarh and the feat of having achieved mastery in deciphering the famous old inscriptions there have been narrated in an earlier chapter. I am intrigued by this aspect of Indraji's life. Twenty-year-olds in small Indian provincial towns were unlikely to have tried to acquire proficiency in reading old inscriptions unless there was something in the air of the times and the town to motivate him. The nineteenth century Junagarh must have been an exciting place to grow up in. The author gives us brief glimpses into it, but I would say that the only limitation of this work is that it does not deal at length on the cultural ambience of Junagarh, Indraji's home ground. The author records that two Dewans of Junagarh, Amarji Dewan and his son Ranchodji Dewan, were interested in knowing about inscriptions even before Colonel Tod's visit to the place in 1822. This was unusual for them because Indian officials of the princely states are not known for their antiquarian curiosities. The Junagarh situation was apparently exceptional and may be due to an element of cultural awakening in Gujarat during that period.

In 1862 Indraji, aged 23, came to Bombay, more or less formally as an assistant of Bhau Daji, a medical doctor and a keen antiquarian. His fieldwork, which was paid for by Bhau Daji, began in 1862 itself: the rock-cut caves of the Western Ghats, and Ajanta and Pitalkhora, a little away from them. He discovered the sculptures of the Satavahana kings at Nanaghat and his reading of the inscriptions in the rock-cut caves enabled the reconstruction of the Satavahana and Kshatrapa dynasties. In 1865–1874 he took himself further afield: Sanchi, Sonari, Udayagiri, Eran, Mandu, Delhi, Mathura, Bairat, Kalsi, Banaras, Sarnath, Allahabad, Gadwa, Kyusinagar, Lauriya Nandangarh, Bodh Gaya, Barabar and Hatigumpha caves of Bihar and Orissa, Puri, Ganjam, Warangal and Kolhapur, as well as Kashmir, Taxila, Peshawar, and Yusufzai, according to the list given by the author. His stay in Nepal was prolonged and his historical researches there were aided by the comparatively new innovation of photography. What is further noteworthy is that he conducted his explorations throughout the year. For him, there was no 'field season'.

Comparison with another travelling archaeologist of the time, Alexander Cunningham, is inevitable. Cunningham focussed on the identification of ancient sites in terms of their modern geography. That was his broad theme. Did any such broad theme run through Indraji's travels or was he motivated by a simple desire to get to know the ancient historical, epigraphical, sculptural, iconographical and other details of the country's past? The author is somewhat silent on this issue, but Indraji was possibly inspired by the later motivation. That he aimed to shape himself as a historian is suggested by the author's learned discussions on his *Early History of Gujarat* (1896) and various contributions to the study of the early history of Maharashtra.

As was reasonable, Indraji interacted closely with James Burgess. The details of the author's discussions on the combined results of Indraji-Burgess scholarly endeavours will require careful study. Burgess was likely to have helped him in procuring some funds from the Bombay government. Funds also came from the Junagarh Nawab after his reputation was firmly established.

In a most important section of the book the author discusses the details of Indraji's fieldwork site by site based mostly on different Gujarati publications. For example, before setting out for Ajanta, he studied the Kanheri caves, and before travelling to Ajanta via Chalisgaon, he copied an inscription at Patan associated with the mathematician Bhaskaracharya and visited Pitalkhora. Ajanta became his training ground after Girnar, and the author refers to his notebook detailing the different Ajanta viharas and attempting the identifications of some paintings. Further, the author draws attention to the fact that in 1871-72 Indraji carried in his tour a formal letter of introduction from the Under-Secretary to the Government of India to various officials and political agents "requesting them to give him every help in the persecution of his research, and take care that he was not molested in copying the inscriptions he might desire to see". The second phase of Cunningham's survey began in 1871, and the fact that the Government of India extended its formal approval to another survey of the same general type undertaken by a native scholar implies that by this time the Government of India had come round to accept archaeology as a legitimate area of investigation and that in this matter there was no suggestion of difference between the natives and the rulers.

As the author reports the death of Bhau Daji at the unripe age of 50, our attention turns to this patron of Indraji. Bhau's grand dream, as the author points out, was to publish a monumental volume on Indian archaeology, and it was with this end that he sent Indraji to various parts of India at his personal expense. The fact that an Indian medical person was able to have this dream in the mid-nineteenth century implies that by this period an element of nationalism had already entered Indian archaeology. It was not a question of knowing merely about the Western Ghats rock-cut caves or the backwaters of Maharashtra and Gujarat. It was a quest for the history of Bharatavarsha as a whole, and it is for this quest alone that Dr. Bhau Daji and his Pandit Bhagavanlal Indraji deserve a much more secure place in the history of Indian archaeology than what has been accorded to them so far.

This volume is like a treasure chest. One can pick up any discovery made by Indraji or any of his scholarly opinions and think at length on its various ramifications: the sites of eastern Malwa, Mathura lion pillars, the second Asokan inscription at Bairat, Ajanta chronology, the chronology of the Vakatakas and Rashtrakutas, the excavations at Sopara and hosts of other issues which make up an Indian antiquarian's life. This reviewer thanks Shri Virchand Dharamsey most warmly for giving us an exquisite scholarly volume on the history of archaeology in western India and for making us aware of the significance of the all-too-brief lives of Bhagavanlal Indraji and his friend and patron Bhau Daji.

16

Newspaper Columns

HINDUSTAN TIMES, AUGUST 29, 2003

1. It is the Archaeology, Stupid!

Considering that only 15 per cent of all the archaeological excavations undertaken in India since Independence are properly published, the submission of a full report on any excavated site in the country should be a matter of great rejoicing among archaeologists. When I read on the internet that the ASI had submitted its report on its five-month long excavations at the site of the now-demolished Babri mosque in the early historic city site of Ayodhya, my initial reaction was that of joy. Whatever might be the original compulsion of carrying out this excavation—this is the first time in the annals of archaeology that an excavation took place under the overall control of the judiciary—the fact was that we would now have a proper report on one of the most important ancient city sites of the subcontinent.

I was also happy because here was at least one case when the ASI could prove its mettle. Its officers could come up with a full report within three weeks of the completion of a full excavation season. Whoever heard of such a thing in Indian archaeology? Could there be more of archaeology under the judiciary in our country please? If what one finds on the internet is right, various people have begun to question the ASI findings. To cast a slur on the findings of what is undoubtedly the best and most dependable professional archaeological organisation in the country is an act of pure political expediency. Whatever we can accuse the ASI of conscious falsification of data cannot be one of them. For those of us who have lived through the Ayodhya controversy through the past decade, it must have been all very confusing. One could understand the utilisation of the issue as a means to get votes. But how did it become an archaeological issue? What, in fact, is the archaeology of a site and how do archaeologists reach their conclusions? As far as Ayodhya is concerned, it is perhaps time one takes a general overview of these matters.

The Brahminical literary tradition regarding Ayodhya is essentially mythological and can't be proved or disproved by archaeology. It was the capital of the Ikshvaku dynasty which in turn belonged to the solar race of the Brahminical cosmogony. Rama and his father were Ikshvaku kings. The *Taittiriya Aranyaka*, part of Vedic prose literature, describes Ayodhya as a celestial city, whereas the *Ramayana* (6th canto of Book I) describes it as a real city. The Buddhist tradition affirms that Buddha spent time here. This, in view of the proximity of Ayodhya to Sravasti where the Jetavana monastery (where Buddha frequently stayed) is archaeologically identified, is probable. Some Jain Tirthankaras have been associated with the site. Such intermingling of religious traditions is characteristic of not merely Ayodhya but of almost all other major city sites of India.

In the early Buddhist sources, the image of Ayodhya is that of a thriving city. Its two names—Saketa and Ayodhya—were interchangeably used, and during the time of Buddha (6th century BC), it was one of the six great cities of India. Ayodhya has been subject to desultory and very limited archaeological investigations since the 19th century. But whatever has been done shows that the Buddhist sources are not wrong.

The circuit of the site is 4-5 km and the large Ramkot segment of the mound covers about 80 hectares. The three prominent mounds, locally known as Mani Parvat, Kuber Parvat and Sugriv Parvat and located to the south of the Tilodaki stream which joins the Ghaghra or Sarayu downstream of Ayodhya, may all be Buddhist religious complexes—the first two of them stupas and the third one a monastery. The old fortification of the city can still be followed in patches, and if my memory serves me right, this fortification passes through the vicinity of both Hanumangarhi and Ramjanmabhoomi. Signs of a ditch outside the fortification are fast disappearing but they are there. On the whole, the image of a large city site during the 6th-7th century BC and later is archaeologically valid.

The earliest occupation of the site goes back to what is known as the Northern Black Polished Ware (NBPW) phase, roughly 800–200 BC. Some areas of the site should contain evidence of occupation during the earlier Black-and-Red Ware period dating from before 1000 BC.

The NBPW marks the phase that witnessed the construction of the fortification wall and the ditch. The history of the site is continuous after that and suggests a prolonged significance for the place—coins, terracotta sculptures and sealings—evidence of the local dynasties and its incorporation in the dominant kingdoms of various periods of northern India.

The site is mentioned in Ptolemy's *Geography* (2nd century AD), a reference which fits in with the find of Rouletted Ware sherds related to the Indo-Roman trade in its 1st century AD level. Ayodhya flourished under the Gupta kings (4th–6th centuries AD), but languished for several centuries in the post-Gupta period when ruled by minor monarchs.

It enjoyed some importance as a part of the kingdom of Kanauj in the second half of the 11th century. Qutbuddin Aybak conquered Ayodhya in the late 12th century when it became the capital of the new province of Oudh. Under Akbar it was a Mughal mint-town and by the beginning of the 18th century, its history was that of the new independent kingdom of Oudh which lasted till 1856 when it was annexed by the British.

The most important archaeological relic now surviving in Ayodhya is an Asokan lotus-form capital that serves as the base of the *Sivalinga* in the modern Nageswarnath temple. The back of the temple stands against a high mound which, if excavated, is likely to find the Asokan pillar, of which it was a part. The quality of this capital is equal to that from Sarnath and shows once again the importance of the place—an importance easily explained by Ayodhya's position on two important trade routes: the one which passed through the Ganga Plain from the west to the east, and the one which led from Sravasti across the Sarayu to the Godavari Valley in the Deccan. The archaeological evidence of these routes is extensive.

As an archaeological site Ayodhya is, thus, far more important than our narrow focus on the Ramjanmabhoomi/Babri mosque would imply. This leads us to the question of how we should judge the veracity of archaeological findings and claims. The answer is really simple: by focusing on where the trenches have been laid and what these trenches have individually shown.

The basic task of any excavator anywhere is to understand the series of depositions of various signs of human activity which have taken place since the mound was first occupied. The story of these depositions is contained on the four walls of the excavated trenches. The excavators are duty-bound to give graphic representations of the layers or signs of various depositions they have found in their trenches. They call these representations 'section drawings'. All archaeological claims have to be checked, first and foremost, in the light of these section drawings.

Any archaeologist worth his salt will also produce a valid cross-section across the excavated area on the basis of his sections in individual trenches. Anything found in the trenches—walls, floor-levels, objects, anything—has to be related to the depositional context in which they occur. This is how we determine if particular structural features are continuous and contemporary or disjointed and do not add up to a pattern.

My impression of the Ramjanmabhoomi mound has always been that it is essentially a structural site. The ASI excavators are likely to have produced many structural features. They must have produced many section-drawings as well so that other people can judge what they have done. I have no doubt that they have done their duty professionally and faithfully. Meanwhile, it is time for us ordinary Indians to realise that there is more to Ayodhya than is suggested by the acrimonious political dispute between two groups of wretched academics and others.

HINDUSTAN TIMES, MARCH 9, 2008

2. The West Knows Best?

One gathers that the Ministry of Culture is going to table a proposal that, if passed by the Lok Sabha, will enable educational research institutes and academic bodies outside India to get loans of Indian antiquities from museums or excavated sites. I wonder if the concerned people in the ministry have carefully considered the implications of this proposal. I am an Indian citizen who earns his living by teaching and researching the ancient Indian past in exactly such an academic body that will be entitled under the new law to bring over anything on loan from an Indian museum or excavated site. I suppose this gives me an insider's point of view on this matter, and it may be worthwhile to lay bare this point of view both for our ministry and the concerned Indian public.

What necessitates the proposal in the first place? The existing set-up does not prevent foreign scholars from coming to India and study whatever ancient object or specimen they want to study. Why should they be permitted to take the objects out of India? All the scientific techniques currently employed to study the different vestiges of the past are available in the Indian laboratories. Any non-Indian keen on applying any of these techniques to an Indian museum object or excavated specimen can do so through a collaborative research project with the relevant Indian science group.

If the foreign-based scholar wants to have the specimen in his own space, there is reason to suspect his motive. The most charitable explanation I can offer is that the foreign scholar concerned is not interested in having an Indian collaborator in this regard and wants the result of his study to be entirely 'West-inspired'. What is also likely in this case is that the result of this research will be in a foreign journal that will not be commonly available to Indians, even in their metropolitan libraries. This means that the result of this study of a segment of the Indian past will be closed to Indians unless they are willing to pay for that article in the online version of the concerned journal.

The reluctance of the Western specialists in ancient India to publish the fruits of their researches in India is well known. To give an example, the Euro-American archaeologists interested in South Asia have been holding biannual conferences in Europe since 1981. With only one exception, the proceedings of these conferences have been invariably published in Europe and America. In most Indian university libraries, they are not available. So, however positive the perception of our Culture Ministry is regarding foreign scholarship in the field of ancient India and its material remains, that scholarship is not meant to be accessible to Indians.

Those concerned, for academic and not-so-academic reasons, that there should be an easier movement of India's antiquities to non-Indian institutions and academic art collections for making foreigners better aware of the richness and variety of India's past, may be told that enough of these specimens is already available in many centres of learning including the private art galleries in the West, where they are on sale.

Occasionally, I have been forced to wonder if some of the finest specimens of ancient Indian art have not already found their way to the rich academic institutions of the West and the collections of their super-rich private patrons. Some years back, a Bangladeshi scholar wrote a detailed monograph on the richly decorated terracottas of a site near Kolkata, basing himself, by his own admission, on what was already available in the US. All that one has to do to get an idea of what related to the Indian past is available in the West is to go through the catalogues put up by the major Western auction houses or published by different museums.

Some governments are known to monitor the appearance of their national antiquities in the international market. A Cambridge archaeological research institute has a specific cell to monitor the illegal looting of antiquity: 'antiquity without context'. Scholars write learned articles on the legal and various other implications of these antiquities. If the present proposal of our Culture Ministry goes through, India will send a clear message to the international antiquity collectors (institutional or otherwise) that its antiquities will now be up for grabs legally—as a 'loan', as long as one can put up an academic and his research as a front. The situation will be a bit like the medical establishments with charitable status that we have in India. All of them have the word 'research' somewhere in their names but it is not really necessary to get any research done.

The proposal has some serious long-term implications for the study of the Indian past through archaeology. All kinds of excavation results fall within the purview of antiquities, and these range from the excavated clods of earth to different kinds of biological materials. If these samples are offered 'on loan' to foreign archaeologists in their own countries, a few things will happen. First, the Indian role in their studies will simply disappear and the results of these studies will also not be easily available to Indians.

Second, the point that has to be driven home is that the study of the past—even its science-based study—is not a universal discipline in the sense of physics, chemistry, mathematics or even economics. It deals essentially with regional data, and the scholarship that has evolved around it does not permit universal postulates, methods or answers. Even when the study of archaeological samples is based on various forensic techniques, themselves offshoots of various sciences, the answer is never one-to-one. For interpretation, there is always a wide arc in which the scholar will position himself, depending on his attitude to the country whose past he is studying.

This is where the element of politics enters archaeology. Socio-politics of the past is a recognised theme of modern archaeological research. What will happen is that this proposal will both aggravate and consolidate a trend which is already here—a trend where the Western archaeologists consider themselves as a group vis-à-vis the Indians. I have been in this game long enough to know that no foreign group can be given unhindered freedom to exert control over a nation's past, even though it is ostensibly for academic reasons. As far as practicable, no nation does so.

THE INDIAN EXPRESS, 9 SEPTEMBER, 2009

3. From Indus to India

Professor K.P.N. Rao and his associates assert, on the basis of their recently published computer studies on the Indus script, that this script has statistical regularities which are in line with other natural languages. Thus, the various signs of the Indus script cannot be explained away as only symbols of different sorts. The latter opinion was expressed by an American group sometime back and apparently taken seriously enough by Rao and his colleagues to undertake their own analysis. That the Indus script represents a language is amply shown by the way its signs were found scratched from the right to the left on an inscribed potsherd from Kalibangan and the way in which the signs were arranged on the seals of Mohenjo-daro.

Further, the rarity with which many of these signs occur is almost a certain indication of the fact that much of the textual corpus of the Indus Civilisation was written, on the analogy of the Indian tradition which continued down to the end of the nineteenth century, on perishable materials like palm and birch leaves.

The basic problem, however, lies elsewhere. There is a conscious attempt in certain quarters to disassociate this civilisation from the later mainstream tradition of Indian/Vedic culture. Historically, the beginning of this attempt can be traced to the period around India's Independence when Mortimer Wheeler proposed that the impetus for this civilisation came from Mesopotamia. Earlier, when India was a jewel in the British crown, there was no compulsion to depict it as an offshoot of Mesopotamian or other contemporary civilisations. The early excavators had no problem hypothesising that this civilisation was deeply rooted in the Indian soil and that many of its features could be explained with reference to the later Indian civilisation.

The current attempts to disassociate the Indus Civilisation from the mainstream Indian tradition have assumed many forms. The term 'Indus Valley Civilisation', which is being increasingly common, suggests that this civilisation was primarily a product of the Indus Valley alone, which is far from being the case. The civilisation is also bandied about as the product of what is dubiously dubbed as the 'middle Asian interaction sphere' and not as a product of a vast region of the subcontinent. Its chronology has been needlessly shortened, suppressing a long and continuous developmental span of about 2500 years in the modern Indian section of its distribution area.

The civilisation is also visualised at the end of a straight arrow-line of wheat-barley-based development beginning in Baluchistan at *c.* 7000 BC, completely ignoring the contribution which came from the east—from the early farming and metallurgical developments in the Aravallis or from the rice-cultivating tradition that began in the Ganga Plain and its Vindhyan periphery in the seventh millennium BC. The famous Sramana image from Mohenjo-daro, which shows the bust of a shawl-wearing man with a meditative expression, is now advocated as belonging to an artistic tradition of north Afghanistan and beyond. Notorious Hindu-baiters are aghast at the thought that anything related to Hinduism could occur in that civilisation, whereas the first excavators' frame of reference for the study of the religion of this civilisation was Hinduism.

That Siva was worshipped in this civilisation is proved not merely by the phallus-shaped stone objects found at Mohenjo-daro and Dholavira but also by the find of an indisputedly *Sivalinga* set in a *Yonipatta* at Kalibangan. If anybody is interested, Bhang and Dhatura, both favourites with a class of Siva-worshippers, occur in the Indus Civilisation.

The battle raging these days is whether there can be a relation between the life depicted in the Vedic literature and this civilisation. Without trying to pull down this debate to the all-too-common Indian level of 'progress versus reaction' syndrome which implies that any talk in favour of Veda-Indus Civilization relationship is a 'right reactionary' proposition (a la Irfan Habib), we note that scholars of the stature of M.S. Vats, R.P. Chanda, B.N. Datta and P.V. Kane had no difficulty in arguing for a relationship between the two.

The opinions which we have noted above and which try to disassociate the Indus Civilisation from the mainstream Indian tradition are endemic in modern First World archaeological literature on the subject and its followers in India. First World Archaeology, as my long familiarity with it tells me, suffers from a sense of inordinate superiority in relation to the archaeologists of the Third World. By allowing it to enjoy a free run in the country as the present archaeological policy of the government does and by allowing it to set up 'Indus Centres' in Vadodara or Pune, grievous damage is being caused to national archaeological scholarship in India.

Appendix

The Comptroller and Auditor General's (CAG) 'Performance Audit' of the Archaeological Survey of India

After such knowledge, what forgiveness ?

T.S.Elliot, 'Gerontion'

The full title of the Report is *Performance Audit of Preservation and Conservation of Monuments and Antiquities, Report of the Comptroller and Auditor General of India, Union Government (Civil), Ministry of Culture, Report No. 18 of 2013*. This is the first time that such a 'performance audit' was carried out in Independent India on the Archaeological Survey of India (ASI) and its related organizations.

The report was prepared for submission to the President of India under Article 151 of the Constitution. The audit was conducted between April 2012 and February 2013 and based on the scrutiny of files and documents related to the following organizations: (1) Ministry of Culture, (2)Archaeological Survey of India, (3) National Monument Authority, (4) National Culture Fund, (5) National Museum, Delhi, (6) Indian Museum,

Kolkata, (7) Salar Jung Museum, Hyderabad, (8) Allahabad Museum, Allahabad, (9) Victoria Memorial Hall, Kolkata, (10) Asiatic Society, Kolkata, (11) Asiatic Society, Mumbai, and (12) Chhatrapati Shivaji Maharaj Vastu Sangrahalaya (CSMVS), Mumbai.

I. EXECUTIVE SUMMARY

The report begins with its 'Executive Summary': why was this topic selected for audit and what it was intended to cover; how was the report organized; what are the highlights of the audit findings and the summary of its recommendations.

The reason why this audit was undertaken is simple. No audit of this kind has been undertaken since Independence, and its aim was to "assist the executive in identifying the reasons behind deficient performance of the organizations in the field of heritage preservation and conservation for enabling effective rectificatory steps" (p. vi). Out of the 3678 centrally protected monuments of the country, 1655 monuments were physically inspected by the audit team jointly with the members of the 24 'Circles' of the ASI. These monuments and sites were selected for joint physical inspection because of their historical significance and geographical distribution. Seven museums (National Museum, Indian Museum, Victoria Memorial Hall, Asiatic Society of Kolkata and that of Mumbai, Salar Jung Museum, and Allahabad Museum) were also jointly inspected. Records of the ASI and its offices, Ministry of Culture, museums and other associated organizations (National Monument Authority and National Culture Fund) for the period 2007-08 to 2011-12 were also 'test-checked' for this performance audit of the ASI.

The organizational scheme of the report is the following. Chapter I incorporates the background information, audit approach, and details of sample selection. Chapters II to X provide the overall audit findings on predefined audit objectives. These objectives were concerned with the themes of preservation and conservation of monuments and antiquities, management of excavation project, funding, functioning of the major museums and their monitoring. Chapter XI examines the issues of governance at the level of the Ministry and the measure of its response to the reports of the earlier committees, court rulings and CAG reports. Chapter XII presents the conclusions along with 61 recommendations.

Highlights of the Report

Attention has been further drawn to the following highlights of the report.

1. There has been no comprehensive survey or review to identify monuments of national importance and include them in the list of centrally protected monuments. Similarly, there is no review of those monuments which have currently lost the status of national importance.
2. There is no ASI database of the exact number of the monuments protected by it.
3. During the joint physical inspection of the monuments, 92 monuments could not be traced. This was out of the total of 1655 jointly inspected monuments. This figure is 'far higher' than the number of untraceable monuments reported by the ASI to the government.
4. The sites which fell under the category of "World Heritage" sites were in many cases subject to encroachments and unauthorized constructions, and there had been no comprehensive assessment of preservation works that were required in the case of these sites.

5. The ASI does not have any updated and approved conservation policy to address the conservation and preservation requirements. In the absence of prescribed criteria for prioritization of monuments requiring conservation works, they were arbitrarily selected for conservation, and in many cases monuments which require structural conservation were not taken up for the work at all.
6. There is poor documentation of the conservation works. "Inspection Notes" on monuments were not prepared by the concerned officials.
7. Although one of the primary activities of the ASI is exploration and excavation of the archaeological remains of the country and their study, less than 1 per cent of the ASI budget is spent on this.
8. Excavation works suffer from poor documentation. The ASI Headquarter, Delhi, could not provide the status of 458 excavation proposals sanctioned in the last 5 years. No data are available regarding the status of pending excavation reports, and numerous cases of excavation proposals were not undertaken or left incomplete.
9. There was no comprehensive policy guideline for the management of antiquities owned by it. The ASI did not set any standard for acquisition, preservation, documentation and custody of objects in its possession. Valuable antiquities were found stored in poor condition.
10. The museums did not perform any better in this direction. There was no proper system of even evaluating and checking the authenticity of objects acquired by them.
11. Accession registers were not properly maintained in all the museums under review. Significant discrepancies were observed in the number of antiquities reportedly available

in Indian Museum, National Museum and Asiatic Society, Kolkata, and those available as per their database.

12. There was no specific policy for systematic conservation and restoration of artefacts.
13. The ASI did not have a database of the total number of antiquities in its possession. The audit team found that 131 antiquities were stolen from various monuments and sites and that 37 antiquities were stolen from site museums. The ASI effort to retrieve these artefacts was ineffective.
14. More than 95 per cent of museum objects lay in reserve collections. There was no rotational system of display in the galleries.
15. There was shortage of staff in all key positions in the ASI and National Monument Authority.
16. On the part of the Ministry of Culture, the governance was lax and found wanting on all aspects of adequacy of policy and legislation, financial management, monitoring of conservation projects and provision of human resources to these organizations.
17. No note has been taken by the concerned authorities of the many previously constituted expert and Parliamentary Committees on the functioning of the ASI and museums.

Specific Recommendations

In addition to listing the above-mentioned 17 limitations, the audit team made about 37 specific recommendations.

1. The list of protected monuments should be regularly updated and reconciled periodically so that there is no discrepancy of data at any stage.
2. Each protected monument should be inspected periodically by a suitable officer. The state of each monument should

be published on the basis of inspection notes and photographic evidence.

3. There should be a clearly laid down policy for notification of sites with contested ownership or occupants. Every such monument may be put in a temporary list till the disputes are resolved.
4. There should be a written agreement with the management of sites with restrictive entries. There should also be a policy for maintaining such sites.
5. Where monuments are used as offices and residences, there should be detailed guidelines regarding changes in them, and the Act should appropriately be revised.
6. There should be a centralized database for all site notifications and records. This document is crucial for establishing encroachment or unauthorized construction at the site.
7. The data related to monuments must be unambiguous and should be put in the public domain.
8. There should be a strategy to ensure time-bound completion of heritage by-laws for all protected monuments.
9. The ASI should define the objective criteria and requirements for selection of sites for final inscription of World Heritage sites.
10. The conservation and management of World Heritage sites should be marked by a systematic approach.
11. The World Heritage sites should be under a separate project for their maintenance and security.
12. The Ministry should develop a comprehensive conservation policy and update its manuals and work code. There should be mandatory log-books for each protected monument to record in detail all conservation efforts.

13. The projects needing funds from National Cultural Fund should be prioritized so that there is an advance comprehensive assessment of funds to be required.
14. There should be guide-lines on 'living monuments'.
15. Documentation on non-living monuments should be properly maintained to stop unauthorized possession and use.
16. The Ministry should frame / finalize the national policy on archaeological excavation and exploration.
17. On the basis of the importance of sites there may be a priority list of excavation projects with fixed accountabilities.
18. There must be clear guidelines for the maintenance and storage of excavated antiquities.
19. These guidelines should be accompanied by an inventory of the excavated antiquities and their locations. This inventory should be put in the public domain.
20. The ASI needs to enhance the use of modern scientific technology, suitably train its officials and an upgraded dating laboratory of its own.
21. Legal framework may be made more contemporary and effective and should be adequate to facilitate restoration of stolen art objects from other countries.
22. There should be proper national-level digitized register of antiquities (in an electronic format as well).
23. This database should be centralized so that all antiquities stored at different localities are available.
24. Regarding stolen antiquities there is scope for more proactive and vigilant roles of the ASI and the Ministry.
25. The Ministry should frame a comprehensive policy for the management of antiquities owned by various central museums.

26. There should be detailed guidelines for the functioning and establishment of site museums.
27. The display of artifacts may be based on rotation.
28. The reserve collection should be properly maintained in suitable storing conditions.
29. There should be clear norms and guidelines for designating a site as ticketed.
30. The ASI should revise rates for ticketing and film-shooting.
31. The Ministry should explore new ways of revenue collection from heritage sites and museums in the light of global practices and standards.
32. The conservation- related works should be provided adequate manpower.
33. There should be coordinating body at each 'Circle' with the representatives of the State governments to check the incidents of encroachments with the help of district and police authorities.
34. There should be regular monitoring of encroachment cases at the highest level in the Ministry.
35. There should be a security plan for each monument, taking into account all its relevant factors and vulnerabilities.
36. There should be a comprehensive security policy for museums.
37. Funds should be earmarked for awareness, interpretation and related activities.

II. CHAPTER-WISE SUMMARY OF THE REPORT

Chapter I

Chapter I is 'introduction' and begins by pointing out that "heritage conservation is viewed as a subject of utmost importance for national identity and also for preserving the knowledge and arts of the past". About a third of the Ministry of Culture's budget is used for the functioning of the ASI and another six per cent was utilized by the country's seven major museums. However, there has been no "comprehensive scrutiny" of the Government's performance of the organizations engaged in the work of heritage conservation.

The Organizations Covered by the Audit

The organizations covered by this audit have been listed in detail in Annexe 1.1.

1. ASI – objectives: survey of archaeological remains and excavations; maintenance and conservation of centrally protected monuments and sites; development of epigraphic and numismatic studies; setting up and reorganization of site museums; conducting expeditions abroad; and training in archaeological work and publication of technical study reports and research works.
2. National Museum, Delhi – set up in 1949 – repository of 2.06 lakh objects with 11 collection departments– archaeology, arms and armour, decorative art, Central Asia, painting, pre-Columbian and western art; manuscript, jewellery, anthropology, numismatic and iconography – 26 exhibition galleries.
3. Indian Museum, Kolkata – established in 1814 – repository of both Indian and non-Indian objects – six sections comprising 35 galleries of cultural and scientific artefacts.
4. Victoria Memorial Hall, Kolkata – established under the Victoria Memorial Act of 1903 and declared as an institution of national importance in 1935. Mainly collection of

documents, photographs, medals, armour, manuscripts, etc. of the British period.

5. Asiatic Society, Kolkata – established in 1784 – declared as an institution of national importance in 1984. Collection of paintings, manuscripts, coins, etc.
6. Salar Jung Museum, Hyderabad (SJM) – established in 1951 – declaration as an institution of national importance in 1961. About 48000 objects, 40528 books and 8556 manuscripts – display in 38 galleries. Collection acquired by a single individual, Salar Jung III, the Prime Minister of Nizam's State.
7. Allahabad Museum – established in 1931 – declaration of 'national importance' in 1985 – 70121 objects and 18 display galleries.
8. Asiatic Society, Mumbai – the Literary Society of Bombay (1804) was merged in the Bombay Branch of the Royal Asiatic Society (1826). A large antiquity collection from Sopara and other west Indian sites.
9. Chhatrapati Sivaji Maharaj Vastu Sangrahalaya, Mumbai (CSMVS) – set up to honour the visit of King George V to India – about 50000 exhibits mostly from India but also some from abroad. Organization private. Receives one-time grant from the Ministry under the scheme "strengthening of museums in Metro cities".
10. National Culture Fund(NCF), Delhi – set up in 1996 with a view to enabling the involvement of the corporate sector, NGOs, State governments, Public sectors and individuals in the task of promoting, protecting and preserving India's natural, cultural and intangible heritage. Given an initial corpus of 19.5 crores, the NCF was to generate and utilize

funds for conservation, maintenance, promotion, protection, preservation and upgradation of monuments protected or otherwise. The task of the NCF also includes imparting training to staff and specialists at all levels in the field of conservation of both tangible and intangible heritage.

11. National Mission on Monuments and Antiquities (NMMA), Delhi. Launched in 2007, as the Prime Minister's declaration to this effect in 2003, the mission was intended to document and prepare suitable database of unprotected built heritage, sites and antiquities through published and unpublished resources and antiquities.
12. National Monument Authority (NMA), Delhi and competent authorities. This came up because the AMASR Act of 1958 was amended in 2010 to authorize the Government of India to constitute a National Monument Authority (NMA) and Competent Authority to scrutinize the proposals for issue of 'No Objection Certificate' for carrying out the repair and renovation in the prohibited area (100 m from the protected area) and for construction and reconstruction in the regulated area (200 m from the prohibited area). This work was earlier carried out by the ASI's Circle offices. The NMA was also required to prepare and approve the heritage bye-laws for all the centrally protected monuments and to present them in Parliament which would help them in assessing the impact of any construction, especially the large-scale projects in the protected monuments which were of national significance.
13. National Research Laboratory for Conservation (NRLC) – the NRLC of cultural property was established in 1976 for research in materials and methods of conservation,

disseminate knowledge in conservation, impart training in curative conservation and developing programs in the field of preventive conservation. Its aims included research for the development of better methods of conservation, technical studies of art and archaeological materials, technical assistance to museums, archaeological departments and other institutions, training, documentation, publications, international liaison, etc. Regional Conservation Laboratory was established in 1986 in Mysore with proposals for further centres in the Northeast, West, East and Central India.

Legal Framework

The Indian Treasure Trove Act of 1878; The Ancient Monuments Preservation Act of 1904; The Ancient and Historical Monuments and Archaeological Sites and Remains (Declaration of National Importance) Act of 1951; The Ancient Monuments and Archaeological Sites and Remains (AMASR) Act, 1958, enacted on 28 August 1958. This last-mentioned act was followed by AMASR Rules 1959. The Antiquities and Art Treasures (AAT) Act of 1972, enacted in September 1972 for effective control over movable cultural property consisting of antiquities and art treasures, followed by AAT Rules 1973, enforceable with effect from 5 April 1976. The AMASR (Amendment and Validations) Act, 2010 prescribes the limits of regulated and prohibited area around a monument.

The Audit Constraints and Objectives

The objectives of the audit were to investigate the adequacy of efforts to identify, document, preserve and showcase proper management of excavation projects, with due documentation, preservation and protection of antiquities and excavated sites;

existence of proper institutional and monitoring mechanism to ensure heritage conservation and for exploring new avenues in the field; effective and efficient functioning of the major museums of the country; performance of the museum movement. Proper financial management.

The sources of audit criteria: all Government Acts, Rules, Regulations.

The audit scope: centrally protected monuments preserved by the ASI. Also, museums, covered audit of National Culture Fund and National Monument Authority.

Audit methodology: entry conference with the Secretary, Ministry of Culture on 16 May, 2012; exit day on 3 June 2013.

Audit sampling, audit constraints:

The following records were not available: records related to details of the monuments along with notification numbers, etc. for the Bengaluru, Bhopal, Chennai, Dharwad, Hyderabad, Lucknow, Patna and Srinagar Circles. Files and records related to preparation of World Heritage site nominaton dossiers, Rani-ki-Vav, Qutb Shahi, Hyderabad; details of integrated management plan for Champaner, Pavagarh. Records related to selection of consultants in 2002 and 2006 for World Heritage Site of Majuli. Report submitted by Shri Prakash Chand, consultant for restructuring and reorganization of the ASI in 2012 and action taken thereon.

Report of the Wheeler committee of 1965 and action taken thereon. Report submitted by the Committee constituted in 2012 to review the security arrangement and assess the performance of private security guards. Information regarding the Kos Minars of Agra Circle. Details of full-time security guards deployed in monuments.

The following details were not available regarding the National Monument Authority:

Files and records related to the appointment and selection of consultants for technical and administrative works. Files and records in respect of the cases where the NMA recommended for rejection of No Objection Certificates(NOCs). Files and records in respect of the cases where the applications were returned seeking more information.

In the case of the National Museum, there was no information on the AA category objects.

Chapter II

Chapter II deals with the 'identification and protection of monuments and their documentation' and begins by discussing the concept of the 'monuments of national importance'.

Monuments of National Importance

The first point to note is that there are no set criteria to define the term 'national importance' either on the Ministry level or on the level of the ASI. Two points are noteworthy in this connection. First, bringing unprotected monuments under the banner of the 'monuments of national importance' is not a continuous process, i.e. the ASI Circles are not instructed to assess if any of the currently unprotected monuments is worthy of being categorised as monuments of national importance under central protection. Secondly, there is also no attempt to 'de-notify' some monuments which were earlier given national importance once but have now lost that significance.

The absence of a reliable database regarding protected monuments is clear from the discrepancy in the number of these monuments provided by the ASI Head Quarter on the one hand

and the ASI Circles/sub-Circles on the other. This discrepancy is sharpest in the case of Delhi Circle where the number of protected monuments given by the ASI central office is 174 whereas the same number given out by the Delhi Circle is 149. According to the ASI such discrepancies are the result of various reorganizations of the Circles which result in the modification of their administrative boundaries. What is implied is that the ASI is indifferent to keeping its records straight and properly verified.

Notification and De-notification of Monuments

The next point deals with the "shortcomings in notification and de-notification of monuments". There has to be a two-month notification period before a monument can be brought under central protection. No firm procedure has been laid down for this process. The Circles can, on the basis of the opinions of the Circle-in-Charge or persons above him, send such proposals with an inspection note by the Circle-in-Charge to the Director General (DG), ASI. The DG, ASI appoints a committee with Joint DG, ASI as chairperson to scrutinise these proposals. The proposals, when thus scrutinised, are sent to the concerned Minister for approval to issue a preliminary notification in the official gazette. The DG-appointed committee held only 4 meetings since 2006, and out of the 78 proposals sent by different Circles since 1996, only 53 were put up for consideration before the Minister. Eventually 34 proposals were sanctioned, and out of these 34, only 2 or 3 were notified till 2012.

Twenty-six de-notification proposals came from the Circles over the past 46 years but the relevant monuments were not de-notified till the end of 2012. The two sites of 'siege batteries with inscription' in Qudsia Garden (Delhi) have been missing since 1971 but proposals for their de-notification were submitted only in July 2012. The notification (2003) of Sat Narain Bhawan (Sadhora Khurd, Roshenara Road) in Delhi was quashed by the Delhi High Court but the monument was not de-notified. The present owners have since then demolished the building but it still continues to be 'under protection' in the ASI books including the list of protected monuments of Delhi on the web.

Information on Location and Actual Condition of Protected Monuments

In some cases the concerned ASI officials were not aware of the exact locations of their protected monuments. For example, the Kashmiri Gate sub-circle of Delhi Circle, could not trace the protected monument listed as "Enclosure Containing the Graves of Lt. Edwards and Others, Murdered in 1857". Such cases suggest that "the mechanism of inspection by the ASI was grossly inadequate. Norms of regular inspection at Circle/Sub-Circle level were absent, resulting in inadequate information about the location and status of protected sites".

Number of "Missing" Monuments

In 2006, the ASI informed the Ministry that 35 centrally protected monuments were not traceable. The same number was conveyed by them to the Parliament in the same year. In 2012 they repeated this number. However, even in the audit sample of 1655 monuments as many as 92 monuments were found missing.

Discrepancies in Issue of Notification

There were instances of more than one monument being notified by the ASI in a single complex. For example, in the Jageshwar temple complex near Almorah under Dehradun Circle, six monuments were notified. In the absence of a uniform standard to recognize a monument as an independent entity, the audit team "could not conclude that security concerns and budgeting needs of monuments were adequately assessed and addressed".

There are also cases where part of the monument was not declared protected. In the Jageshwar group of temples, again, 118 of its 124 monuments were not protected.

Double Notifications

Some monuments were notified twice. Hauz Shamsi in Delhi was notified both as Shamsi talab and Iron Hindu pillar.

Monuments Included in the List but Not Finally Notified

It was found that some monuments, although placed on the list of centrally protected monuments, were not notified in the gazette till February 2013.

Instances of Hasty Notification

There have been cases where the building to be notified is under encroachment and/or under legal dispute and notifications in such cases involved the ASI in litigation. The examples are *Tamluk Rajbati* (Tamluk, West Bengal) and "Clive's House, Dum Dum" (near Kolkata).

Monuments Protected by Both Centre and State

Gaps in the notification process are also highlighted by the fact that some monuments have been notified both by the State and Central governments. For instance, the Dharanikota ruins of Guntur were notified both by the ASI and the State Department of Archaeology and Museums, Andhra Pradesh.

Repeated Notification and De-Notification

The case of the five monuments commemorating Anglo-Sikh battles of Mudki, Sobraon, Saragarhi, Ferozeshah and Misriwala in Ferozepur, Panjab is interesting. They were notified in November 1918 but de-protected in 1927 and 1962. They came once again under notification proposal in 2006. These monuments are currently under State protection.

Monument Protected before Completion of 100 Years

The case of the Cooch Bihar palace which was notified in 1982 before the monument completed its 100 years is an example.

Antiquities Protected as Monuments

Some canons, guns, *jhoolas*, statues, etc. are being protected as monuments but no reason is offered why they should be treated as monuments and not as antiquities.

Categorisation of the Monuments

The monuments declared of national importance have to be grouped into 8 categories in accordance with their scale of importance under Section 4A of the AMASR (Amendment and Validation) Act of 2010: category I – World Heritage sites (WHS); category II – tentative list of WHS sites; category III – identified for inclusion in the WHS list; category IV – ticketed monuments (apart from the WHS–related range); category V - list of monuments to be 'ticketed'; category VI – living monuments with large number of visitors/pilgrims; category VII – monuments in the urban/semi-urban limits and in the remote villages; category VIII – other category as the Authority may deem fit.

This categorisation has been operative since 2011, but except for Guwahati Circle, no 'Circle' has yet categorised its protected monuments.

Access to the Protected Monuments

The ASI has been unable to stop unlawful activities at many protected monuments. "During joint physical inspection, we found that in many monuments, electrical points, loudspeakers, fans, etc. were also installed by unauthorized persons to facilitate these activities" (p. 22). Such activities were noticed in Delhi Circle itself in the ancient mosques of Palam and Qudsia Garden.

In some cases there was closure of monuments, in full or parts, without the approval of the DG, ASI. There are also monuments in areas which do not have free public access. This was a violation of the act providing free access to nationally protected monuments. *Equally curious is the fact that certain centrally protected monuments were open only to specific religious groups. In 7 protected monuments of Lucknow, non-Muslims are not allowed to enter the monument.*

Also widespread is the use of monuments for other purposes by the ASI (cf. offices of various kinds). The changes in the character of these monuments as the result of such uses (cf. electrical fittings, toilets, water pipes, etc.) "are not consistent with the original character of these monuments". This is applicable also to some WHS places (Red Fort, Delhi, Fatehpur Sikri) where sensor-fitted taps, hand-driers, etc. have been installed as VIP facilities. Some monuments are also used as residences of officials and security guards. Although there was a system to allow cultural events at some prescribed monuments for specified fees but there have been cases where some monuments have been used as venues for cultural functions without the approval of the DG, ASI. For instance, *Ramleela* was organized without the DG ASI approval even in Red Fort, Delhi.

Inspection of the Monuments

The audit team found that the practice of regularly inspecting monuments at various levels

> had been completely given up in recent years. There were no inspection notes available on records detailing the inspections done by the DG, ADG and Director (Conservation) and other officers during the period covered under Audit. Similarly at the Circle level there were no inspection notes available on the visits of Superintending Archaeologist (SA) and Deputy Superintending Archaeologist (Dy.SA). The inspection notes by Sub Circle in-charge and sometimes by the SA were available on record only in relation to proposals of detailed estimates of conservation works .... In the absence of inspection records, it was not possible for us to ascertain the date on which a particular site was last visited. In the context of monuments being untraceable and being encroached upon, this documentation was of utmost importance (p. 27).

Maintenance of the Information in Respect to the Monuments

There was no compilation of data regarding the notifications of monuments: "the ASI stated (July 2012) that the list of monuments with date/number of notification was not being maintained and hence was not available." The Dharwar Circle, for instance, had 299 protected monuments but the details are available for only 110 of them. The Ministry (May 2013) accepted the fact that they had no Management Information System (MIS). Equally interestingly, the digitised documentation of the monuments and archaeological sites, which is being undertaken by the Indira Gandhi National Centre for Arts (IGNCA), did not match with the information supplied by the Circles on the same monuments and sites, the discrepancy being confined mainly to the co-ordinates (latitude and longitude) of the monuments and sites. The CAG report clearly underlines the fact that the variation of a single second in the co-ordinates will mean a difference of 1.85 km in location, and if the difference is that of one degree, that will mean 111 km difference in the actual location. The CAG team further points out that there are discrepancies in the areas defined by the notification, the discrepancy in the case of the Besnagar tank and temple remains being more than 27 acres. The area as per notification is 76.73 acres whereas according to the Circle it is 49.02 acres. The Audit team found out that an updated inventory comprising the brief details of all the protected monuments including their notification number, site plan, brief history, photographs, etc., which should be maintained by all Circles is being maintained and updated only by the Aurangabad Circle. There was an ASI proposal in 1997 to edit and publish the inventories of all Circles but the project has been given up and the inventories of only five Circles were published. As far as the joint physical inspection with the Revenue Department to ascertain the exact area of a monument is concerned, joint survey was carried out only in the case of 409 monuments out of the total of 3678 protected monuments.

National Mission on Monuments and Antiquities (NMMA)

As per records, India has about 5 lakh unprotected monuments and about 70 lakh antiquities in different areas of the country.

The NMMA was set up by the Prime Minister in August 2003 to create a suitable database on built heritage and sites and antiquarian remains. It was launched only in 2007 and has shown so far a dismal performance record: documentation of only 80000 monuments and 8 lakh antiquities till 2012 (3 lakh antiquities were already registered with the ASI). Only 2823 entries out of 8.80 lakh available entries were uploaded on the website. The NMMA was established in Tilak Marg after incurring an expenditure of 53.28 lakh and its subsequent shifting to Red Fort cost the exchequer a further sum of 30.52 lakh. This shifting also resulted in the loss of data. Only 16 per cent of the funds which were released by the government for the NMMA could be utilized by this agency.

What leads to significant doubts on this score is that the data compiled by the NMMA are based on secondary sources and that those data need validation. The NMMA request to do primary surveys has not (till November 2012) met official approval.

Heritage Bye-laws

According to the AMASR (Amendment and Validation) Act 2010, the Government of India was

> required to prepare heritage bye-laws in respect of each monument and protected area. The heritage bye-laws shall also include use of building material, façade, roofing pattern, colour, height, built-up area, usage, stilt parking, underground construction, drainage systems, roads and service infrastructure like electric poles, water, sewage, excavations and such other factors which may be necessary within the prohibited areas and regulated areas of the protected monuments and protected areas". These

bye-laws have to be submitted to NMA for approval and the Competent Authority was required to put them on their website(p. 33).

What has been achieved is that the heritage bye-laws for only two monuments (out of a total of 3678 monuments) have been prepared. Till June 2013, there was no time-limit fixed for preparation and approval of heritage bye-laws.

Chapter III

This chapter is concerned with the management of World Heritage Sites. In 1972 the general conference of the UNESCO adopted a convention concerning Protection of World Cultural and Natural Heritage. It was sought to encourage around the world the identification, protection and preservation of cultural and natural heritage which may be considered as of outstanding value to humanity. India ratified this convention in November 1977, delegating to the ASI the role of nodal agency for nomination of WHS sites to the UNESCO. The ASI has 19 WHS sites under its control.

Procedures for inscription of a site as WHS are as follows. A site is first put in the tentative list of the UNESCO, which is maintained in India by the Archaeological Survey of India . It has to remain in this list for one year or more. Before being sent for final nomination to the Ministry, there has to be a 'nomination dossier' containing the details of the site including its conservation plan and Site Management Plan. After the Ministry approves, the dossier is sent to World Heritage Centre (WHC), UNESCO, Paris, for further evaluation and approval. This is followed by a site visit by the UNESCO's advisory bodies (International Council of Monuments and Sites or ICOMOS or International

Union for Conservation of Nature – IUCN). This site visit results in recommendation for 'rejection'/ 'deferral'/' referral' (further information)/ inscription (acceptance of the proposal). The UNESCO then gives the final verdict and the site/monument is inscribed in the list. The label 'Outstanding Universal Value (OUV)' is given in the nomination dossier.

The ASI's status as Nodal Agency is not ratified by any written order. Out of the 53 proposals submitted by the GOI to the UNESCO, only 19 protected monuments have been inscribed. Till 1993 there were 16 'dossiers', all prepared in-house by the ASI. The work was mostly outsourced to 'consultants' after that. The audit team "noticed a steady decline in acceptance of proposals" with the increased use of consultants. None of the three proposals submitted in 2007-12 were sanctioned, and of these three, two proposals were outsourced to consultants at a cost of 79.84 lakh. The Ministry appointed an Advisory Committee in the Ministry in November 2011, and although the Committee has met seven times since its inception, there has been no successful case till November 2012.

There were no defined criteria to put a site in the tentative list where it has to remain for a year before being put up for nomination. There were no standard procedures to be followed or prioritisation in the case of the sites on the tentative list. The UNESCO guidelines suggest the review and updating of tentative lists every ten years. The ASI has so far failed to update this list.

Further, the audit team found that

> the activities constituting preparation for final inscription included only selection of consultants for nomination dossiers and Site Management Plans. There was no project or concerted effort to develop the site *per se* (p. 33).

The selection process of consultants for preparation of nomination dossiers and Site Management Plans differed from case to case. Both the ASI and the States appointed consultants, revealing "lack of transparency, tendering irregularities and undue favour to consultants"(p. 39). In all the five cases submitted in recent years (Santiniketan, Majuli, serial nomination of Harappan sites, extension to Pattadakal, and Rani Ki Vav), the sites have not yet received the WHS status although Rs. 1.76 crores were spent on the related consultancies.

Santiniketan: the consultancy was awarded jointly to Ms. Abha Narain Lamba and Shri Manish Chakravorty at a cost of Rs. 35 lakhs in May 2009. The nomination was submitted in 2010 but withdrawn after assessment by ICOMOS. Also, audit irregularities.

Majuli, Assam: consultancies to Ms. Nalini Thakur and Shri Surojit Jaradhara in 2004; to Ms. Poonam Thakur and Shri Rohit Jigyasu in 2008 for Rs. 16.84 lakhs, and to Shri Suryanarayan Murthy (M/s Kshetra) in 2012 for Rs. 28 lakhs. The three proposals were found technically incomplete by ICOMOS. Also, audit irregularities.

Serial Nomination on Harappan Sites: consultancy to Shri Ranesh Ray in March 2009 for Rs. 65 lakhs. Proposal deferred. Also, audit irregularities

Extension Proposal to Badami and Aihole to the Pattadakal Group of Monuments: consultancy assigned to Shri A Ramanathan and Shri Ranesh Ray for Rs. 14 lakhs (subsequently enhanced to Rs. 24 lakhs). In 2011 the work awarded to M/s Adel Dronah for Rs. 31.56 lakhs in 2011. The work was not ready till December 2012. Also, audit irregularities.

Preparation and Implementation of Site Management Plans

As per UNESCO's Operational Guidelines of 2008, the preparation of Site Management Plans, which give a total inter-related perspective of the conservation and management of the sites, was mandatory for WHS sites. In the case of the 15 out of the total number of 19 WHS sites under the ASI, these plans were either not ready or implemented at the site.

Four consultants were appointed for Integrated Management Plan(IMP)/Comprehensive Conservation Management Plan(CCMP)/Site Management Plan (SMP) for 4 sites for an amount of Rs. 2.92 crores, out of which Rs. 2.59 crores have already been paid to the consultants, although these have not been finalized or implemented. The consultants concerned are Nalini Thakur (for Hampi, receiving 14.25 lakhs in 2004-5), Gurmeet Rai (for Red Fort and Ellora Caves, receiving Rs. 91.46 lakhs in 2005 for Red Fort and Rs. 94.60 lakhs in 2007 for Ellora Caves) and Abha Narain Lambah(receiving Rs. 92.13 lakhs in 2007 for Ajanta Caves).

The audit team found that the foregoing SMPs or Site Management Plans

> were poorly prepared and hence could not be implemented. The plan provided no guidance to the Conservation Assistants and other field staff about the actual management of the site. It was mostly an academic monument discussing concepts and theoretical approaches for management of the site (p. 42)

Site Inspections at the World Heritage Sites

The point to note is that the grant of WHS status to a site "did not translate into better availability of facilities, funding and staff for these sites" (p. 42). There was no distinction in Conservation,

Security and Maintenance between the WHS sites and other sites. In 2007-2012 the total revenue collected from the WHS sites was Rs. 320.03 crores, with their relevant expenditure being Rs. 243.96 crores.

All the relevant details are summarized in Annex 3.3 and Annex 3.4 of the report.

Status of Amenities at World Heritage Sites

At Khajuraho, Fatehpur Sikri and Champaner, the cases of unauthorized constructions were, respectively, 628, 194 and 107. There have been encroachments at Red Fort, Qutb Minar, Bhimbetka, Hampi and Champaner. Nine WHS monuments including Taj Mahal, Red Fort and Qutb Minar were partly closed to the public. No audio guide service was available at 14 out of 19 WHS sites including Ajanta, Ellora, Khajuraho and Red Fort. There was no CCTV at 16 (out of 19) sites. Hand-held metal detectors, scanners, etc. were not available at 7 sites. There was no facility for the disabled at 6 WHS sites including Humayun's Tomb and Bhimbetka.

The audit team followed up the above-mentioned facts by undertaking 3 case studies. The details in each case are noteworthy.

The basic revenue and staff details of the Taj during the last five years are as follows: Rs. 84.90 crores earned as revenue (31 lakh foreign tourists and 173 lakh domestic tourists) and the total of Rs. 7.55 crores spent on its preservation and conservation during this period. The number of ASI and Central Industrial Security Force (CISF) personnel appointed at the Taj during this period were 128 and 275 respectively.

The SMP of *the Taj* was not finalised and the maintenance of the site was found inadequate by the audit team.

Status of public amenities like drinking water, toilets, ramps and wheel-chairs: these amenities were available but Braille signage was not available. Most of the Indian visitors entered through West gate but there was no cloak-room facility for them. Parking facility was located about 1 kilometre away from the entry points. There was no audio guide facility for Korean, Japanese, Chinese and Gujarati languages. Within the premises of Taj Mahal, encroachment was noticed near Khan-i-Alam's Bagh, but it was not even officially recorded by the ASI. There were 24 unauthorized constructions around the Taj but only one of them was demolished. An old temple next to the outside boundary on the eastern gate, which was constructed without authorisation, has been left undisturbed. The outer boundary of the Taj was in bad shape, with large nails dug into the wall and animals tethered to them. The left side boundary wall at the eastern gate was left un-conserved. Equally seriously, the audit team "noticed cracks in the outer walls, broken stones fixed in the wall, missing designs, use of cement in the wall, seepage, fixing of plastic pipes, and broken jalis"(p. 46)

Even inside the monument conservation and preservation works were not satisfactory: fading plaster at the main entrance to the monument; instances of missing inlay designs and seepage; careless maintenance of the garden. The mosque and Mehman Khana, on the eastern and western sides of the main mausoleum respectively, had missing plaster, missing designs and seepage. In the main mausoleum of the Taj, there was lack of coordination between those who did the chemical work and the Circle office: a missing design from the main iron gate; floral designs turned black; and cracks in the design. Although a stone conservation laboratory was set up in Agra in 2006 by the Science Branch of the ASI with the help of UNESCO to check the quality of stone before it was used, the quality of the Rs. 1.35 crore worth of stones used for the stone flooring of the campus between 2007-008 and 2011-12 was not checked in the laboratory.

The ASI earned Rs. 25.59 crores as revenue from Red Fort in the last five years and spent Rs.15.77 crores on its preservation and conservation during the same period. The numbers of private security guards and the CISF personnel employed at Red Fort were 119 and 317 respectively. Curiously, there were two 'notifications', one in 1913 and another in 2002, to take over this monument. This has led to Red Fort being treated as two protected monuments in some ASI records. However, the inventory of the Delhi Circle treats the second notification as supplementary to the first notification and treats Red Fort as a single monument.

The 'unauthorized closure of monument or its parts' included *Hamam*, Moti Masjid and *Baoli* which were permanently closed without the approval of the competent authority. There were also restrictions for the general public to visit Mumtaz Mahal, Khas Mahal, Dewan-i-Khas, etc. *Takht* was not open to close viewing both at Dewan-i-Am and Dewan-i-Khas.

The residential quarters of a large number of the ASI and CISF (and private security guards as well) personnel (including the DG, ASI), and a large number of ASI offices were inside Red Fort which also harboured unauthorized temples and *mazars*.

Audio guide facilty, introduced in 2012 , was available only in English and Hindi. Visitors had to walk more than 1 km to reach the ticket counter either from the nearest bus stop or the authorized parking lot. There was no CCTV at Lahori Gate and there were no CCTV and metal detectors at Delhi Gate. No security system was in place for the vehicles entering Red Fort. There was also no Braille facility for the visually impaired people.

The Comprehensive Site Management Plan of the Red Fort prepared by the consultant Gurmeet Rai at a cost of Rs. 91.46 lakhs did not mention such an important issue as overhead wiring and was considered impractical, resulting in wasteful expenditure.

The contract for managing parking at Red Fort was awarded to an ineligible contractor in September 2010. From July 2011 the contractor stopped depositing the money, and the total dues against the contract were Rs. 1.14 crores on 31 May 2012, including electricity charges and penalty.

The organizers of the annual *Ram Leela* celebrations did not abide by the terms and conditions of permission. Not only did the ASI not take any action against them but also waived off the prescribed fee of Rs. 50,000 stating that it was a religious function.

There is a long list of the improper conservation works in Red Fort . There were marks of bad conservation and dilapidated conditions of stones at Lahori Gate. There were seriously damaged stones at the entrance to Naubat Khana. Its floral design was replaced by a multi-coloured patch-work. The use of cement was noticeable. The *Takht* was seemingly protected by a net to ward off pigeons and bats, but the birds in any case kept on pouring through the net which also destroyed the overall aesthetic appeal of the place. There was widespread seepage on the ceiling of the *Dewan-i-Am.* Its rear wall showed cracks and the brackets holding the structure were seen falling off.

In *Dewan-i-Khas,* chemical conservation was needed, and the effort to restore its original design on the walls was abandoned midway. In *Saon* and *Bhado Pavilion,* there was lack of uniformly done chemical conservation work. There was a lot of wild vegetation in the garden between the two pavilions, which also required the restoration of pathways and water channels. The *Jalis* of Jaffar Mahal, a red sandsone structure were found broken and this combined also with the unwelcome elements of vegetation, seepage and cement work. Stones were missing in several places; there was no plaster on the bricks and there was water-logging on the floor. The stones and some portions of the *baoli* were broken and mixed with a lot of vegetation. The garden adjoining the *baoli* was found in a totally unkept condition. The GE building of the British era, now occupied by the office of the National Mission on Monuments and Antiquities had a number of modern gadgets installed and its pathways showed poor maintenance.

Summary Comments on State of Preservation and Conservation of Red Fort

> The above observations make it clear that this symbol of our national pride and a World Heritage Site, had not received the care and protection it required. The ASI officers highlighted the issue of shortage of funds and manpower. However, we found that a comprehensive assessment of preservation works and funds requirement had never been carried out. No concrete efforts were made to obtain funds through the NCF or any other alternative route. No proposal for comprehensive preservation of the Monument was put up to the Ministry for separate funds allotment. The Ministry on its own failed to take any initiative in this direction (p. 59).

The third case study involved Ajanta from which the ASI earned a revenue of Rs. 4.97 crores in the last 5 years. The total expenditure on the caves during the same period was Rs. 7.19 crores. The number of private security guards was 42, but there was additional patrolling by the State police. Its SMP (Site Management Plan) was not complete, although it was under preparation by an external consultant , for which Rs. 81.10 lakhs were already spent.

The security was lax in the sense that no scanners and CCTV were available at the site. The public amenities at the site did not include toilet facility for the disabled, audio guide, and cloak rooms.

The identification and execution of the projects of chemical conservation at Ajanta were the responsibility of 'Field Laboratory at Ajanta' under Science Branch. However, there was no inventory of the paintings and there was no laid down documented policy for their chemical cleaning or conservation. There was also no mechanism for monitoring and evaluating the results of cleaning and fixing responsibility against defective execution.

In 1992 (Phase 1) and 2003 (Phase 2), the Government of India signed an agreement with Japan Bank for International Cooperation (JBIC), leading to an expenditure of Rs. 17.03 crores in both phases. The aim was to conserve the paintings and develop the Ajanta area.

The unstable micro climatic conditions inside the caves play a major role on the conservation of paintings. The painted plasters fall off. The falling of white pigments were noticed in the ceiling of Cave 2. Further, the thick coat of protective layers applied on the paintings by earlier conservators accumulated dust, soot, excreta of bats, etc., leading to the prevalence of haze over the paintings, hiding their original glow. The careless use of solvents also caused chalkiness on the paintings. The impact of visitors inside the caves increased humidity and carbon dioxide concentration, both detrimental to the preservation of the paintings.

CHAPTER IV

Chapter IV deals with preservation and conservation works.

Lack of Conservation Policy

The last definitive edition of John Marshall's 'conservation manual' dates from 1923. *The Manual of Archaeological Survey of India* was supposedly published in 1984 and *Archaeological Works Code* of the government possibly dates from the same period. The process of revising the two last-mentioned publications began in August 2011 but did not yield any result till December 2012. The upshot is that the ASI does not have a comprehensive modern conservation policy, thus making the performance evaluation of conservation and preservation works 'highly subjective'.

Ineffective Monitoring by the ASI HQ

The Circle offices were responsible for the conservation and preservation work on monuments. The Superintending Archaeologist of the Circle (SA) was supposed to report any irregularity during the execution of the work and for maintenance of the documents. The DG, ASI was eventually responsible.

The audit team noticed the following irregularities: (1) no mandatory requirement for inspection by the SA; (2) inspection notes not prepared after inspections; (3) absence of complete documentation of the work estimates; (4) faulty budgeting of the conservation works resulted in inclusion of extra items; (5) delays in completion of works; and (6) non-preparation of completion reports along with photographs after conservation.

Status of Monuments as per Joint Inspection

The joint inspection of the audit team with the Sub-Circle personnel of the ASI covered 45% of the total number of protected monuments, and some of the many conservation issues and concerns may be listed as follows: (1) plaster coming off in

63 monuments; (2) vegetation not properly cleaned in 73 monuments; (3) large cracks in 33 monuments; (4) 64 monuments (cf. Jantar Mantar, Delhi, Hampi temples, Bidar fort, Lakshmi Narayan temple in Aurangabad Circle) needing urgent chemical cleaning/treatment; (5) cement found to be used in 64 monuments (cf. Taj Mahal, Fatehpur Sikri, Jhansi Fort, Gulara Mahal in Bhopal Circle, Baijnath temple in Dehradun Circle); (6) seepage noticed in 63 monuments; (7) design/structure of the monument changed or decoration obliterated in 33 cases; (7) the use of modern tiles changing the original appearance of the monument in 3 cases; (8) parts of the wall or the domes of the monuments broken long ago but unrepaired in the case of 40 monuments; (9) original stones and tiles missing from 16 monuments; (10) garbage/*malba* lying in monument in 12 cases; (11) in the case of 3 monuments (cf. vaulted roof of upper and lower basement in the Viceregal Lodge in Simla), the roof of the monument found damaged, showing big cracks.

Conservation Documentation

Maintenance of log-books of conservation works: earlier the ASI used to maintain log-books on each monument detailing the conservation efforts including the details of materials used, changes made, architectural drawings. This practice has been discontinued.

Lack of coordination between structural conservation (by the Circle office), environmental conservation (done by the Horticulture branch) and scientific conservation or chemical cleaning and treatment done by the Science branch: this along with the 'abysmal state of monitoring by ASI HQ' has meant that the details of expenditure incurred and the conservation efforts made on a particular monument are not available in a comprehensive manner. The Directorate of Horticulture intimated that it had 504 gardens in its care whereas the combined figure from its four divisions stood at 504. The total number of gardens with original designs was claimed to be 60, a figure that did not match with the response of its own divisional offices.

In this context a very important point has been made by the audit team: "in the absence of any authentic documentation, it was difficult to fix responsibility for a damaged portion, incomplete work of repair, etc."

Maintenance of work related records: the following records have to be maintained according to the Archaeological Work Code: (1) cash book (form TR4); (2) measurement book (form CPWD-92); (3) tenders and contract documents like contractor's ledger, tender sale and opening register, agreement and security deposit register; (4) estimates including register of deposit works and sanctioned estimates; (5) other work records like register of tools and plants, unpaid wages and cement stock register, etc.

Also to be maintained is the documentation of the details of labour in the form of labour registers, daily labour report, etc.

> We observed that many Circles, viz. Delhi, Agra, Lucknow and Bhuvaneswar did not maintain the register of works and thus year-wise details and item-wise expenditure incurred on various conservation works could not be ascertained (p. 67).

Irregularities in planning of conservation works: these are clearly noticeable in the following cases: (1) *criteria for selection of monuments for conservation*: no procedure of assigning priorities across various works in Circles/Branches; Marshall's procedure ignored; work taken up mostly in ad hoc manner as per the subjective assessment of the officials. (2) *Monuments without special repair work/annual maintenance work*: no special repairs taken up in 765 monuments and no annual conservation work taken up in 691 monuments during the period of audit; no prescribed criteria for planning and prioritisation of monuments for conservation work; no information available from the ASI HQ on special repairs and annual repair works. (3) *Delay in submission of Revised Conservation Programme* (RCP): delay of up to 69 days for the submission of the RCPs by the Circles/ Branches to the DG ASI (the due submission date – by February of the year for the works which were to be carried out in the next financial year). This initial delay had a cascading effect and led to further delays in the subsequent stages. (4) *lack of scrutiny of RCP and expenditure statements from the Circles/Branches at the ASI HQ*. For example, special repairs of Hauz Khas complex in Delhi Circle reflected the estimated expenditure at Rs. 14.63 lakhs in 2010-11, and further requirements for 2010-11 and 2011-12 were Rs. 83.81 lakhs and Rs. 10 lakhs respectively. (5) *Works approved but not carried out without explanation*: in 5 Circles 103 works, worth Rs. 5.57 crores and approved by the DG ASI, were not carried out during the year. (6) *Estimates without assessment*: difference between the approved budget and expenditure ranged up to 266% but the DG ASI did not seek any explanation. Approved budget and expenditure did not tally in Delhi, Srinagar and Jaipur Circles. (7) *Works carried out without being included in the RCP*: 30 works worth Rs. 4.54 crores and 8 works worth Rs. 23.29 lakhs were carried out respectively in Delhi and Goa Circles without inclusion in the RCP. (8) *Inclusion of non-plan items in plan budget heads*: in 4 Circles the RCP submitted for special repair works (Rs. 10.37 crores) included works of recurring nature such as clearance of vegetation, grill fencing, works on pathways, etc. Expenditure on maintenance of the gardens related to WHS sites and the ticketed monuments was wrongly booked under the plan heads. An amount of Rs. 17.97 lakhs was spent in 2007-08 by Science Branch on such recurring items as laboratory equipment, running of laboratories, and annual maintenance contract of the equipment, all non-plan items. (9) *Inclusion of plan items in non-plan budget heads*: in 2011-12 the special repairs of the Flag Staff Tower (Delhi ridge) cost Rs.7.04 lakhs, involving the dismantling of the old decayed plaster, laying of thick lime plaster on the monument and laying of thick concrete on the terrace. The routine annual work could be approved by the SA but special repairs needed the approval of the DG ASI, which was not recorded. (10) *Office expenditure through conservation budget heads*: office items including computers and stationary were purchased from the budget head of minor works (non-plan) in as many as 176 Sub-Circle offices as no budget was provided to these Sub-Circle offices under the head of office expenses. (11) *Incomplete works*: cases were noticed where the special repair works remained incomplete. The conservation work of the Vittala temple in Bengaluru Circle, which began in 1999-2000, was left incomplete. (12) *Unauthorised expenditure on unprotected monuments*: Delhi Circle incurred an expenditure of Rs. 16.67 lakhs on Jama Masjid, an unprotected monument. Unprotected temples were repaired by Dehradun Circle and Ranchi Circle got a Jharkhand government rest house (Kolhan Rest House) repaired. Similar cases were noticed in Hyderabad, Thrissur and Bengaluru Circles.

Improper Conservation Works

The audit team singles out the following monuments. (1) Saraswathi temple, Singanathanahalli, Bengaluru Circle: badly in need of conservation and proper access. (2) Krishna complex, Hampi, Bengaluru Circle: the main entrance and stone wall of the temple developed cracks along with other structures inside the complex. The bazaar mandapa in front of the complex also needed conservation. (3) Underground Siva temple, Hampi, Bengaluru Circle: water from the adjoining fields entered the temple leading to water logging inside. (4) Fort at Vatakkakottai, Chennai Circle: the ASI has closed one of the mandapas by building walls around it with a door and using it as a store house, thus completely altering its original appearance. (5) Fatehpur Sikri: expenditure of Rs.7.45 lakhs for conservation work of Mint House at Fatehpur Sikri, out of the official sanction of Rs. 15.72 lakhs (in 2005-06) had to be written off because of sub-standard work. No rectificatory action has been taken since then. (6) Sangagiri Fort, Chennai Circle: the reconstruction of Bastion/ Fort wall and the revetment wall of this fort, Chinnakavaudanur, Salem Sub-Circle at an expense of Rs. 13.61 lakhs in 2006-2010 remained in a damaged condition even after the execution of conservation work. (7) Krishna temple in a part of Donka with Gopuram, Kalyanamandapam and masonry built tank, Kalyanamandapa, Hyderabad Circle: this needed complete repair and conservation, the necessity being felt as early as 1977. In 2003-04 the dismantling was sanctioned for Rs.60 lakhs and the work was complete in 2006. The DG ASI sanctioned in July 2006 Rs. 3.48 crores for the reconstruction of the mandapa. The foundation work scheduled for completion in by July 2006 was completed in August 2009. By March 2012 the work was completed by spending a further sum of Rs. 3.55 crores. The lack of proper planning and change in foundation design led to a huge increase in the cost of reconstruction and delay in the completion of the work. (8) Baisgazi Wall, Maldaha, Kolkata Circle: the wall had recesses at regular intervals, but while restoring the northern part of the wall the ASI left no recesses. While restoring the western side of the wall, the recesses were left in place. The conservation work changed the original appearance of the monument. (9) The patch wall done with plain bricks marred the appearance of Jor Bungalow of Vishnupur where all the four side walls were made of decorated bricks. (10) The Yellow Mosque of Murshidabad (Kolkata Circle) was painted white, thus leading to a complete change in its appearance. (11) The arcaded verandah on the right side of the ancient palace of Raja Suchet Singh, (Ramnagar),Srinagar Circle, was converted into a lounge with bathrooms and kitchen, and a portion was used as office. (12) In 2006 the ASI built an extra circular vedika or drum on the existing vedika of the Amaravati stupa, thus altering the original appearance of one of the most important stupas of the country. (13) The shape and appearance of St.Angello Fort, Thrissur Circle, were both changed by using cement concrete in the monument. (14) The lack of monitoring by the Circle resulted in improper and still incomplete conservation work on the Tripolia gate in Delhi. The very appearance of this gate was changed.

Preservation and Conservation Work by External Agencies

Except Delhi Circle, all ASI Circles carried out conservation and preservation work departmentally. The ASI Works Code or the ASI Manual has no provision for conservation work getting done by external agencies.

However, *Delhi Circle was getting all its works executed through external contractors.* In recent years external agencies like INTACH, Aga Khan Trust, etc. were given monuments for conservation. As the ASI does not have any guideline/laid down criteria regarding the qualification and minimum experience in the related field, the selection of the agency was done on a case to case basis. The CAG report cites three cases where external agencies carried out conservation and preservation work without monitoring by the ASI.

(1) *The ASI agreement with the Aga Khan Trust through NCF in April 1999 for the conservation, research documentation, reinstating of water systems and illumination, apart from the restoration of gardens of Humayun's tomb. In 2007 the ASI entered into another Memorandum of Understanding with Aga Khan Trust for Culture (AKTC) for the conservation of protected monuments within the Humayun tomb complex. The AKTC was responsible for raising the necessary funding through domestic or international donors without any financial responsibility on the part of the ASI. The audit team learnt in January 2013 from the person-in-charge of the sub-Circle that the ASI had no monitoring role in the matter. As per the MOU, the ASI had given up its responsibilities in the conservation and preservation work regarding Humayun's tomb.*

(2) *The conservation work on five monuments in the Lodi Garden complex was carried out by the INTACH in 2006. The work was given without any formal agreement or work order to the INTACH because the ASI thought that it was overburdened with works related to Commonwealth Games. The Delhi Circle was supposed to supervise the work. In October 2009, it was noticed that the work carried out by the INTACH was inferior and faulty. In July 2011 an expert committee appointed by the DG ASI found the work to be of poor quality and unacceptable because of poor workmanship, use of inferior material and poor supervision and management. It was also doubted if any repair work was carried out on the flat roof as claimed in the utilisation certificate.*

The INTACH took no corrective action till November 2012 nor did the ASI blacklist the agency or impose fine on it.

(3) *The ASI entered into an MOU in November 2009 with Global Vaish Organization (GVO) for the maintenance of Ugrasen ki Baoli, a centrally protected monument of national importance in Delhi. This MOU was not vetted by Ministry of Law and Justice. The MOU was initially supposed to be between Delhi Pradeshik Agarwal Sammelan but unaccountably shifted to GVO. The initial proposal came through NCF which however was not a party to the agreement. The Project Implementation Committee was not formed till 2012.*

We noticed cases where meetings were held in the monument and no action was taken by the ASI. Without any assessment of GVO's performance, the MOU was renewed for five more years in January 2011. During the joint physical inspection we found that GVO was running an office in the premises from the porta cabin erected to stock the literature, stationery, computers, etc. The chowkidar was residing in the monument permanently. The monument was in a bad condition and there was no water in the Baoli any longer (p. 83).

It was clear that the ASI had no formal procedure "for appointing, regulating or monitoring the work of external agencies deployed for the preservation and conservation of centrally protected monuments" (p. 83).

Unauthorized Conservation Works by External Organizations

Table 4.2 (p. 84) gives the list of such works: Maharaja Ranjit Singh's summer palace in Amritsar (work done by Panjab Heritage Tourism Promotion Board at an expense of Rs. 2.17 crores; lakes of Kirat Sagar and Vijay Sagar and tank at Barua Sagar near Jhansi (work done by Uttar Pradesh State Government, developing a picnic spot and utilizing the water for irrigation and drinking purposes); Jama Masjid and Amin-ud-daula's Imambara, Lucknow (Hussainabad Trust, Lucknow, added wood and glass work, electrification and wooden framework to the monuments to give them a modern look).

Registration of Contractors

The rules are clearly laid down. Paragraph 3 of the Manual of the ASI mentions that the registration of contractors in the ASI would be done at the Circle/Branch office, if the contractor concerned wanted to operate within its jurisdiction. In case a contractor wanted to operate in more than one Circle/Branch, the name would be registered with the DG, ASI who was also supposed to receive half yearly statements giving the details of the contractors.

The ASI HQ intimated that they were not registering any contractor, nor were half-yearly reports available on the contractors. Delhi Circle was registering contractors without verifying their credentials.

Non-recovery of Worker Cess from Contractors: According to the Delhi Building and Other Construction Workers (Regulation of Employment and Conditions of Services)Rules 2002, cess at the rate of 1% of the cost of construction is to be collected and remitted to the Delhi Building and Other Construction Workers Welfare Board after deducting the cost of collection of cess. The total expenditure incurred by Delhi Circle on the conservation of ancient monuments in 2007-2012 was Rs. 64.64 crores. No worker cess was deduced from this amount.

Conservation Works Carried Out through National Culture Fund

Two lists of selected 36 and 100 centrally protected monuments were supplied in 2000 and 2007 respectively by the ASI to the

NCF for requesting funding from donors. The NCF was required to select monuments from the lists supplied by the ASI. However, there was no defined priority in the lists, and monuments outside these lists (Jantar Mantar and Taj Mahal) were selected by NCF without giving any reason. The NCF drafting of MOUs with public and private sector organizations was found to be poor and without any legal vetting (by the concerned ministry) and deadline. The details of the item-wise expenditure were not maintained by NCF, thus negating the link between the expenditure and the concerned monument.

Role of the ASI in the Maintenance of Living Monuments

Paragraph 26 of John Marshall's conservation manual defines a living monument as a monument which was in use at the time of notification. Section 6 of the AMASR Act 1958 ensures that the central government may enter into an agreement with the owner of such monuments "for its maintenance and custody and may restrict the owner from destroying, removing, altering or defacing the monument or to build on or near the site of the monument." The audit team found that " the ASI failed to enter into formal agreement with owners of all such living monuments"(p. 86).

It was further observed that the present owners of the monuments carried out changes in the monuments without the approval of the ASI destroying its original look and appeal.

> Instances were noticed where the trusts/private persons managed these monuments and carried out works in the nature of painting of walls by modern enamel paints, fixing of ceramic tiles and electrical equipment, etc. altering the aesthetic value of the monument. Such examples were the mosque in Qutb Minar, the ancient

> mosque of Palam in Delhi Circle, Shey monasteries, Hemis monasteries in Leh Mini Circle, Bara Imambara and Chhota Imambara in Lucknow Circle and the churches in Goa Circle (p. 87).

Environmental Conservation

A separate garden branch was created in the ASI in 1952, its main functions being "designing, laying out, renewal and maintenance of gardens and enclosing the areas proposed for development besides providing effective entrances and exits" (p. 88). The Directorate of Horticulture was based in Agra (81 gardens) with three other horticulture divisions in Delhi (186 gardens), Mysore (126 gardens) and Bhubanesvar (132 gardens). The Agra division was headed by the Chief Horticulturist with the rank of SA whereas the officers in charge of the three other divisions (Deputy Superintending Horticulturists) held the rank of Deputy Superintending Archaeologist. Administrative anomalies were clear: the garden-in-charge of Hyderabad was also in charge of the Buddhist remains at Sankaram in Vsakhapatnam, which was about 600 km away. The Deputy Superintending Horticulturist of the Delhi division was responsible for all the gardens from Jammu and Kashmir to Daman and Diu. "As a result, monitoring was ineffective in most of the gardens. The gardens were either not maintained at all or were left to gardeners/labourers without any supervision" (p. 88).

> There was no information available with the Horticulture Branch on the original structure, flora and fauna and other decorative features of the historic gardens. There were many gardens around Mughal monuments whose layout and other features were reasonably well documented. However, we did not notice any such

garden being maintained with due consideration of its original design (p. 89).

The ASI was unable in many monuments to ensure the flow of water in fountains and water channels. Both these were important features of Mughal gardens. There was no evidence of the ASI's efforts to document or develop heritage gardens through proper research.

There were 50 gardens in Delhi Circle as against its 174 centrally protected monuments including the gardens attached to various offices. During the last 5 years the number of gardens taken up for annual maintenance were between 25 and 37. The Horticulture Branch failed to maintain even the existing gardens.

Even the gardens of the WHS sites such as Red Fort and Humayun's tomb were not properly maintained. The Horticulture Branch attributed this poor maintenance of gardens to lack of human and financial resources. No concrete efforts were made by the DG ASI in this direction. There is no budget and accompanying manpower to improve the quality of the ASI gardens.

Chemical Conservation and Functioning of Science Branch

The principal function of the Science Branch of the ASI (established in 1917) was the chemical treatment and preservation of museum-exhibits and other antiquities. Its Director, based in Dehradun, had three divisional offices at Bhubanesvar, Hyderabad and Indore and 11 zonal offices around the country and three laboratories at Dehradun, Agra and Ajanta.

In 2009-10 only 149 monuments were taken up for chemical treatment, accounting for only 4 % of the total protected monuments. There was no system in place for regular inspection of monuments to assess their need for chemical treatment. The monuments were selected for chemical cleaning without objective assessment, prioritisation and documentation. In Dharwad Circle, 19 monuments were selected for chemical cleaning and treatment from 2009-10 to 2011-12 but only four proposals were taken up during this period. The details of the work being carried out were not maintained at any level.

Coordination with Structural Conservation

Structural conservation of a monument should precede its chemical treatment, but there have been cases where the reverse had taken place, leading to the wastage of funds. The chemical treatment of Sawan Bhado pavilion (Red Fort, Delhi) was carried out by the zonal office in 2010-22 (Rs. 3.98 lakhs) whereas the structural conservation of the same monument in 2011-12 cost Rs. 21.63 lakhs.

Functioning of Laboratories

In many cases the chemicals and other consumable materials went waste. Chemicals were purchased but could not be utilized before the expiry of their shelf lives. Among the other deficiencies one may note that 4 out of the 9 laboratories in Dehradun were non-functional for the last ten years. Stock registers for scientific equipment and chemicals were not maintained. There was no work-register and there was no organized system to order chemicals.

Cases of Bad Conservation of Chemical Treatment

Mural paintings were found damaged in Lepakshi Temple (Hyderabad Circle) and a few other places. There are other instances of shoddy chemical treatment.

The Case of Kos Minars

There were 110 *Kos Minars* in 5 Cicles: 63 in Chandigarh, 8 in Jaipur, 15 in Agra, 23 in Lucknow and 1 in Delhi. The joint inspection of 40 *Kos Minars* revealed that many of them were encroached upon, missing or were in urgent need of preservation. The *Kos Minars* as a separate category of monuments were never researched and analysed by the ASI. They are being destroyed almost at will by private parties. Only a minuscule amount of the total conservation budget of a Circle is generally spent on the *Kos Minars*.

Chapter V

This chapter examines the issues of excavation, epigraphy and survey.

The importance of conducting ASI-sanctioned excavations is well-known. *The audit team found the following deficiencies in the ASI's discharge of excavation duties.*

Inadequate Documentation and Management Information System

There was no centralised information about the functioning of the Central Advisory Board of Archaeology (CABA), grant of licenses, reasons for rejection of proposals and status of accepted proposals. The records of only a few CABA meetings were available.

National Policy on Archaeological Excavation and Explorations

In December 2009 the Prime Minister expressed the need to formulate a national policy on archaeological excavation and explorations. A CABA committee finalised a draft document in this regard and submitted it to the DG ASI on 23 December for approval. In November 2012 these guidelines were still in the draft stage and the file received with the Ministry's queries was untraceable at the HQ, ASI. There is no time-frame to finalise this policy.

Provision for Mandatory Archaeological Impact Assessment

There was no provision to assess the archaeological impact of various developmental activities. Assurance was given to the Parliament on this score in 2007 but no progress has yet been made in this regard.

Expenditure on Exploration and Excavation Activities

Less than one per cent of the total budget of the ASI was spent on these crucial activities. The option of obtaining funds through NCF was not explored.

Selection of Sites and Grants of Excavation Licenses

In 2007-12, a total of 728 proposals was received from the ASI officers (130) and others in the universities, State departments, etc. (458). There was no transparency in the grant of excavation licenses and recommendations by the CABA.

Some excavated sites were re-excavated without availability of the report on earlier excavations (cf. Rupar, Patne, Raja Vishal ka Garh, Chandraketugarh). Some sites were notified but excavations were not undertaken. For instance, Chankigarh, a protected site in Patna Circle, has never been excavated despite being notified much earlier. In some cases excavations take us because of "VIP references", the most recent case in this regard being the ASI excavations at Daundia Khera (Lucknow Circle) in search of buried gold. Some approved excavation proposals were not undertaken at all, and in some cases they were even left incomplete. In 2007-08, Chandigarh Circle had proposed excavations at the stupa site of Asand in Haryana, and although there has not been any excavation at the site, Rs. 14.98 lakhs were spent "on acquiring computer, camera, photo-material, stationery and kitchen-articles, etc." Some excavations (cf. Benisagar, Singhbhum, Ranchi Circle, Dholavira, the famous Harappan site in Kutch) have been left incomplete. The number of ancient mounds as protected sites is 221, but many of these mounds were not fenced. Some of them were also under cultivation. Further, the excavated sites of the ASI were not being maintained and properly preserved with the result that some of these sites have become untraceable.

The neglect of excavated sites may be best seen at Kanganahalli near Sannati (Bengaluru Circle). Large-scale excavations at Kanganahalli were conducted by the ASI in 1996-2002. The condition of the site has been described by the audit team:

> Despite incurring an expenditure of Rs.1.42 crores for the site, during joint physical inspection we found that the excavated parts of the Stupa and the panels were lying scattered in the open, subject to the vagaries of the nature, water had accumulated in many parts and black patches had appeared on the panels, some panels were covered with plastic sheets to prevent rain water. However, moisture had accumulated and was damaging these panels. DG, ASI in June 2012 had instructed that temporary shelters be provided for the Ashoka Panel and other excavated parts of the Stupa. But this was not done (December 2012). Only a cloth shed was provided for the Ashoka Panel after the visit of Union Minister Shri Jairam Ramesh (August 2012). We also found that the activities of the site were not being carried out with due care. An unsuccessful mending work was carried out on the panels by using non-magnetic steel rod and epoxy

> resins, without proper testing. The Ashoka Panel was repaired by the ASI leaving it damaged. The inventory of the parts was unavailable at the site. We also found that while making replicas of some panels in 2012, the ASI had used fiber glass as mould instead of softer alternatives like latex. The mould left some glass pieces stuck in the curves of the friezes. The ASI officials then used chemicals followed by oil to remove them, leaving the limestone panels discoloured and damaged. Despite assurances from the Minister of Culture (May 2012) in response to a reference from Shri Jairam Ramesh, Minister of Rural Development, the site remained uncovered and neglected (pp. 111-113).

The monitoring of excavations is conspicuous by its absence. Of the 56 pending excavation reports related to the period before 2007-08, only 25 were submitted (September 2012). Some reports have been pending for 57 years. Latest consolidated position of pending reports was not available on record. For the 113 excavations/exploration works undertaken by the ASI in 2007-08 to 2011-12, report was submitted only in 12 cases.

The reasons given by the ASI for non-publication of the reports was not acceptable to the audit team. This team further noticed that

> no inventory had been maintained centrally, on an All India basis, in the ASI for recording all the artifacts, antiquities and sculptures found and collected during excavations, explorations or village to village survey. In many cases... the excavated antiquities were not accessioned and found dumped in the ASI Circle offices, monuments and store rooms (p. 117)

Regarding the other activities related to excavation and exploration, it may be noted that 'village to village survey' has been given up due to the shortage of manpower and the Underwater Archaeology Branch has become defunct due to the lack of specialized manpower. The Building Survey Project was set up in 1977 to survey buildings of the 16th to the 19th centuries but there are no recorded reasons for not finding the reports suitable for publication. The Temple Survey Projects of Bhopal and Chennai submitted reports on 5 projects (1984-2011) for publication but nothing has materialised in this field. There is also a huge backlog of publications in Prehistory Branch, Nagpur. Technologies such as Ground Penetrating Radar (GPR), Magnetic and Resistivity Survey, Global Information System (GIS) and Global Positioning System (GPS) are important in modern archaeological research, and the ASI and the IIT, Kanpur, signed an MOU in 2007 for application of scientific techniques in archaeology. 30 ASI officials were trained in these scientific techniques (plain surveying and GPS and GIS) in 2007 at a cost of Rs. 11.60 lakhs. Only two of these officials were subsequently involved in excavations which tried to use these techniques.

Status of Work and Human Resources for Epigraphical Studies

The headquarter of the Directorate of Epigraphical Studies was Mysore and its zonal offices were in Chennai, Nagpur and Lucknow. The post of its Director has been vacant since 2006. Two posts of Superintending Archaeologists have been vacant since 1998 and 2004. The number of people working in the Branch was 25 whereas the sanctioned strength was 45. 1725 epigraphic items were collected between 2007-08 and 2011-12. The *Annual Report on Indian Epigraphy* was published only up to 1997-98. At the end of March 2012, 43464 volumes of this report were lying unsold. South Indian inscription volumes in

Tamil, Telegu and Kannada were published on the basis of inscriptions collected up to 1955. No work on north Indian Sanskrit inscriptions has been possible in recent years due to the paucity of staff. Only 7 volumes of *Corpus Inscriptionum Indicarum* were published. The Chennai zone of the Epigraphy Branch collected (1991-92 to 2011-12) 5440 epigraphic items, but only 2383 items (collected up to 1998-99) were transcribed. The remaining 3057 items remained untranscribed. The transcription and publication of Telegu inscriptions collected in 1936-38 were not yet done and the editing of Telegu inscriptions collected in 1939-45 also remained to be done. South Indian inscriptions collected in 1916 and 1905 were yet to be transcribed and published. The Epigraphy Branch, Nagpur, was concerned only with Arabic and Persian inscriptions and had deciphered 297 of the 367 inscriptions collected in 2007-08 to 2011-12. The Lucknow zonal office, maintained at the expense of Rs. 1.04 crores in 2007-08 to 2011-12, contributed no inscription to the annual report on Indian epigraphy. There was a delay up to 122 years in the publication of the annual report on Indian epigraphy.

There were 72000 estampages of inscriptions in the epigraphy directorate. The Chennai zonal office had 3105 such estampages but no provision for storing them in climate-controlled situations.

Capacity Building and Research in the ASI

The audit team's conclusion is the following:

> Failure on the part of the ASI to acquire and use modern equipment and to develop a laboratory of its own for dating and analysis of the archaeo-materials had adversely affected the capacity building and research activities of the ASI (p. 121)

The audit team made a survey of the Harappan sites of Dholavira, Rangpur, Rakhigarhi, Rupar, Sanghol, Lothal and Kalibangan and observed dismal conditions everywhere. Proper maintenance was absent at all of them and there were unauthorized constructions and encroachments at most of the places.

Similarly, some sites of Asokan rock edicts were studied.

> Joint physical inspection revealed that the ASI was not properly protecting and conserving these Ashokan Rock Edicts. One of the worst cases of poor conservation was found at the Rock Edict at Udegolam in Dharwad Circle where to protect the rock, big pillars were erected on the rock itself thus damaging the Rock Edict (p. 127).

Even where roof was erected over the edicts, as at Junagad and Nittur, it was noticed that this did not prevent the rainwater from coming in. In Delhi, the grill fencing did not protect the edict from being touched by the visitors and performing some kind of rituals at the spot.

Chapter VI

This chapter is concerned with the management of antiquities for which the Ministry did not have a comprehensive policy:

> There were no standards for acquisition, preservation, documentation and custody of objects (p. 131).

The Central Antiquity Collection (CAC) was established in 1960, but it was noted that "the acquisition, documentation, storage conditions, physical verification and security of antiquities of CAC was grossly inadequate" (p. 133). The storage of antiquities stored at Purana Qila and Safdarjung Tomb was found deplorable. The ASI can also compulsorily acquire antiquities but no antiquity has been compulsorily acquired till date. The museums did not evolve a coherent acquisition policy. In December 2007, the Victoria Memorial Hall entered into an agreement with the Ravindra Bharati Society, a registered Society in West Bengal, to acquire about 5000 paintings. Till November 2012 the status report of only 878 paintings was complete but no conservation work on them was undertaken. There was no benchmark for selection of items offered as gifts. There were no targets and no time-frame for completion of the work of registration of antiquities. There was no monitoring of the progress of this work by either the ASI or the Ministry. There was no system to verify the genuineness of the objects acquired. The best practice in this regard was followed by the Chhatrapati Shivaji Maharaj Vastu Sangrahalaya where the objects were first examined by a Curator and then placed before the 'exhibit evaluation committee'. The final approval was done by the board of trustees.

Accession and final verification of art objects in some important museums left much to be desired. All the audited museums—Indian Museum, National Museum, Asiatic Society, Allahabad Museum and Salar Jung Museum—apparently gave conservation a low priority. *Nearly 40 % of the manuscripts of the Asiatic Society were in poor condition and the conservation laboratory of National Museum was conserving only about 0.25 per cent of its antiquities annually.*

The best practice in this field was observed at CSMVS (or former Prince of Wales Museum, Mumbai) where all the objects in possession of the museum are regularly surveyed to assess their need for conservation. The objects are categorised as per their condition and prioritised for treatment.

Research and development were assigned low priorities in the scheme of our museums. Indian Museum, National Museum and Asiatic Society (Kolkata) did not undertake any research work.

Digitisation and Documentation of Art Objects

There was no documentation of objects taken away from the country before 1947. The absence of documentation is also true of the objects taken out of the country before the implementation of the AAT Act 1972. A part of the Stein collection of antiquities comprising 700 objects was given on loan to the V&A museum, London where this collection is listed as the property of the ASI. Two giant Nazrana Gold Mohurs of the Nizam collection of jewellery were with the Indo-Suez Bank of Geneva, but in the absence of proper documentation on the ownership of these coins, the ASI could not get them restituted.

The ASI collection of antiquities stored in 'sculpture sheds', Circles, stores, Excavation Branches and 44 Site Museums did not have a digitised database.

> ... the ASI was not aware of the total number of antiquities in its possession as no database or inventory of antiquities had been prepared by the ASI. Branch-wise lists were also not available with the antiquity branch at the ASI HQ (p. 142).

The status of documentation in the museums was no better. In any case, the work was far from being complete in all of them including the site museums.

Stolen and Seized Antiquities

In 1976-2001, the number of stolen antiquities retrieved from foreign countries was 19. They came through various means such as legal means, indemnity agreement, voluntary action and 'out of court' settlements. Since 2001 there has not been a single case of retrieval.

> We found that the ASI had never participated or collected information on Indian antiquities put on sale at well known international auction houses, viz. Sotheby's, Christie's, etc. as there was no explicit provision in the AAT Act 1972 for doing so" (p. 144)

Regarding the seized antiquities and court cases also the ASI was found to be devoid of any initiative.

As far as the export of antiquities and the shifting of antiquities are concerned, there was hardly any control, and "in the absence of these controls, the entire procedure for the grant of the non-antiquity certificate was completely open to the risk of malpractice". The ASI 'Site Museums' also needed proper guidelines and criteria for their establishment. In many cases the existing sculpture sheds have not been converted into site museums. Antiquities are stored in all sorts of places and conditions (p. 150 for a list of the status of antiquities). At Benisagar (Singhbhum) antiquities were kept in the staff quarters.

> During physical inspection of the Data Bank by audit in June 2012, we noticed that while shifting from Purana Qila to Red Fort, 60 cabinets out of 120, containing valuable records (original registration certificates) of the Data Bank were severely damaged. In the absence of proper space, another 66 cabinets were kept open in the gallery, exposed to heat, air and dust which deteriorated the records beyond recovery. The data bank was estimated to have 4.5 lakh records, but during the digitisation work of the National Mission and Monument Authority, only 3.5 lakh records were produced as the rest were damaged by rodents (p. 155).

In the case of the exhibitions held abroad, a "Fine Art Handling Agent" (FAHA) was appointed by National Museum. The audit team noted that the Museum failed to take adequate steps to recover compensation from FAHA for the objects damaged in connection with the exhibitions.

Under the 2004-05 scheme of modernising the museums in 'metro cities', an outlay of Rs. 100 crores was earmarked for National Museum, Delhi and Indian Museum, Kolkata. Even after a lapse of more than 8 years, these museums failed to submit detailed project reports.

CHAPTER VII

The theme of this chapter, 'financial management', is tied to the grants made by the Ministry of Culture to the ASI and related offices. In 2011-12, the budgeted 'Plan' expenditure of the ASI was Rs. 152 crores whereas the budgeted 'non-Plan' expenditure was Rs. 287 crores. The actual expenditures under the two headings were Rs. 171.58 crores and Rs. 275.26 crores respectively. The activity-wise expenditure in 2007-2012 was as follows: 'Others-Establishment: 56 %, Site Museums: 2% , Excavation Projects: 1%, and Conservation Projects: 41%. There was a distinct gap between the plan budget proposed by the ASI and that allotted by the Ministry. In 2007-2012 the Ministry's reduction of the budget proposed by the ASI varied from 26% to 44%. In 2009-2012 the excess of expenditure by the ASI with reference to the original allotment by the Ministry ranged from 13% to 27%.

The budgeting process in the ASI was inappropriate and the Circles/Branches were not diligent in working out the budgetary requirements. One of the offshoots of such a casual approach is that the conservation needs of certain important monuments were neglected on the ground of the paucity of funds. In 2007-2012 the ASI generated a revenue of Rs. 422.46 crores which contrast with the Pay and Accounts Office record of Rs.431.78 crores.

The number of 'ticketed monuments' during the period of the audit was 116 but there were no specific criteria or guidelines in declaring a monument ticketed. The whole process was arbitrary and ad hoc.

There are other issues: non-revision of rates for film-shooting; delay in remittances of government money, diversion of funds from Plan to non-Plan expenditure, irregular excess expenditure, unrealistic budget preparation, etc.

Among other acts of financial indiscipline, National Museum kept government money in the personal account of two officials between October 2005 and August 2007. National Museum also did not charge the prescribed market rate of license fees from National Museum Institute, The Handicrafts and Handlooms Export Corporation of India Limited and M/s Khatirdari Catering Services in violation of the terms and conditions of Ministry of Urban Development (p. 168).

Chapter VIII

Manpower Management, the theme of this chapter, involved shortage of manpower in the ASI (percentage of vacancy 28.9), capacity building for conservation, vacancies and shortfalls in technical cadre, shortage of monument attendants, uneven distribution of work, engagement of technical personnel in office work, and undefined areas of hierarchy and reporting.

The efforts to fill the vacant posts resulted in several bottlenecks including the appointment of consultants for routine office work, failure to obtain status of a scientific department, etc. The latter issue is remarkably intriguing. *In October 1989, the Ministry of Human Resource Development designated the ASI as a "science and technology department". However, to be formally designated as such, information on the scientific and technical achievements, functions, activities and research of the Directors and Chief Horticulturist was to be submitted to the Ministry in prescribed pro-forma. Till November 1912 the ASI was unable to put together this information and thus it could not be included in the framework of a Science and Technology institution.*

The functioning of the Regional Directorates , established in 2009 to guide, supervise and control the field offices, turned out to be a dismal failure as they were found functioning without supporting staff. The museums were also understaffed. Irregularities have been clearly underlined by the audit team in the selection of members of the National Monument Authority (pp. 175-176).

Chapter IX

This chapter deals with the security of the monuments and antiquities, beginning with the issue of encroachment and unauthorised construction in and around monuments. *The protected monuments have been under encroachment by individuals, private organizations and even government departments.* In April 2012, the ASI informed the audit team that 249 monuments were under encroachment. The audit team found that the correct number was 546. The government was the encroacher in 46 cases. There have been unauthorised constructions in the 'prohibited' (100 m from the protected limits of the monument) and 'regulatory' (200 m from the protected limits of the monument) areas of the protected monuments. According to the Amendment of the AMASR Rules 1959 (Amendment and Validation, 2010) a distinction had to be made between the constructions in the prohibited and regulatory areas of a monument on and after 16 June 1992. The ASI had no information in this regard. The audit team traced 9112 cases of unauthorised construction (in 98 cases by the government departments/agencies) in the prohibited and regulatory areas of the protected monuments. The Amendment and Validation Act 2010 of the AMASR Rules 1959 authorized the central government to constitute National Monument Authority and Competent Authority to deal with the permission required for repair/renovation in the prohibited area and construction/re-construction in the regulated area. The formation of the NMA has been delayed and the process has not yet (September 2012) been complete. The process of issue of No Objection Certificate (NOC) involves the following steps: application is made to the Competent Authority; the Competent Authority informs the NMA of the application within 15 days; the NMA decides either in favour or against the application within 2 months; within one month of the NMA decision, the Competent Authority would either grant permission or refuse. The audit team noticed systemic lapses in the system and thus "could not conclude that the NMA and Competent Authorities were able to discharge their functions efficiently and effectively" (p. 187)

The details of the security system currently in vogue in monuments and museums are then reviewed by the audit team which noticed serious lapses in the system. For instance, "no security guards were found deployed at 1468 centrally protected monuments by our teams" (pp. 187-188). It was also found that the CCTV system and the system of 'fire safety' were not operational in many cases. The CSMVS, Mumbai, set the best example in this regard.

CHAPTER X

This chapter examines the issues of "awareness, interpretation and amenities" which are very important in the light of the fact that "a protected monument or site would carry little meaning to common people, if there were not enough resources to interpret and explain the cultural and historical significance" (p. 195). However, the present set-up was found deficient on many scores including the availability of publications, notice-boards and maps of the sites, including the places of WHS. In 72% cases there was no drinking water and in 82% cases there was no toilet facility. The ASI was also indifferent to the possibility of online booking of tickets to encourage more visitors to the sites.

CHAPTER XI

This chapter highlights the fact that the Ministry of Culture has by and large been indifferent ("ineffective governance and stewardship of Ministry") to the deficiencies of the whole structure of archaeological research and heritage management under the ASI, one of its subordinate offices. *Inordinate delays in carrying out measures coupled with improper financial management and inadequate monitoring have put the ASI in a complete mess.* The Ministry has also been completely indifferent to the recommendations of the earlier committees including the Mirdha Committee of 1984, the Parliamentary Committee of 2005 and the Moily Committee of 2010. For instance, the Mirdha Committee recommended that the ASI "should be treated as an academic institution with highly specialised duties and be accorded the status of scientific and technical institution enjoying autonomy in its functioning" (pp. 209-210*). The notification for declaring* *the ASI as a Scientific and Technical Institution was issued in 1990 but it was never implemented.*

The Ministry also completely ignored the recommendations of the committees appointed to examine the functioning of various museums including National Museum. For instance, the Varadarajan Committee recommended in 2004 that 20% of the objects of each section of National Museum must be verified each year so that all objects were verified in a five year cycle. There has been no physical verification of objects of National Museum since then.

Further, the audit team noted that "there were instances where no action was taken by the ASI even after the directives of the Hon'ble Supreme Court of India and the High Courts of the States"(p. 217). Two clear cases of indifference to the judgements of the highest court of the land have been cited in the present report. In one case, the Supreme Court annulled the listing of 43 centrally protected monuments as Karnataka Waqf Board properties in 2004. *The implications of this judgement have been ignored by the ASI.* In another case, the fire crackers used in the local festivals near the Tenkailasanatha temple in Thrissur Circle were damaging the mural paintings of the temple, and the Supreme Court judgement (2005) prohibiting the use of fire-crackers resulting in noise levels above 125 decibels was similarly ignored.

The judgements of the various High Courts met with the same fate. The Rajasthan High Court ruled in 2004 against the 66 cases of unauthorised constructions in the protected area of Jaisalmer fort. The relevant constructions were not removed.

The ASI displayed the same level of indifference to the government audits ("regular transaction audit of the Headquarters of the ASI and the Circles and Branches" – p. 218) *and opinions of people.* For instance, the Minister for Rural Development, Shri Jairam Ramesh, informed the Minister of Culture regarding the conditions of the site of Kanganahalli in Karnataka. He dubbed the ASI's conservation efforts at the site as "vandalism masquerading as archaeological conservation". He also called the maintenance of the tomb of Hasan Shah Suri and Sher Shah Suri at Sasaram 'atrocious'.

The ASI smoothly swallowed all such observations without any perceptible trace of unease.

Chapter XII

There is a brief summary of the findings of the Report in this chapter. The basic formulations are the following:

(1) "The most significant failure of ASI related to its core function of field archaeology that included excavation, survey and publication of excavation reports" (p. 221).

(2) "Exploration and preservation were crucial functions of the ASI; however, a comprehensive policy for these areas had not been formulated"(p. 221).

(3) "To ensure effective protection of monuments and sites it was imperative to update policies, publish inventories and fully document monument details. However, these activities had not been completed by the concerned entities. The National Mission of Monuments and Antiquities had also failed to fulfil its purposes in a time-bound manner. This Mission lacked direction, vision and appropriate strategy" (p. 221).

(4) "In the context of these weaknesses, encroachment of monuments and unauthorised constructions were widespread. Further, in the absence of comprehensive planning and organizational weakness, there was no

coordination among the three major wings of ASI, responsible for structural, chemical and environmental conservation" (p. 221)

(5) "Regarding the financial management of ASI, we noted that the funds allocated to ASI for its mandated activities were grossly inadequate" ... The manpower management was marked by critical shortages leading to negligible supervision of works and inadequate security"(p. 222).

(6) "The ASI was unable to implement the provisions of the Antiquities and Art Treasure Act effectively and the incidence of an illegal export of antiquities was rampant"(p. 222)

(7) "We observed significant shortcomings in the functioning of the museums. The museums did not have any benchmarks or standards for acquisition, conservation or documentation of the art objects possessed by them. The mechanism for evaluation of acquired objects to verify their genuineness was absent in all the museums audited by us ... Poor documentation of the acquired artifacts and the failure to introduce the digital technology for documentation coupled with the absence of physical verification made the artifacts vulnerable to loss. The security system at the museums provided a grim picture in the absence of effective surveillance systems at the sites" (p. 222).

(8) "We also noted that many shortcomings related to thew functioning of the ASI had been highlighted through the recommendation of various expert Parliamentary committees. However, we also noted with distress that these red flags were largely ignored by the Ministry of Culture. In our opinion urgent measures were required to completely overhaul the ASI in the light of its mandate and to restore this organization to its distant former glory" (p. 223)

The report has been signed by Roy Mathrani, Director General of Audit, Central Expenditure, and countersigned by Shri Shashi Kant Sharma, Comptroller and Auditor General of India. The report has been consistingly well documented with its wealth of charts, tables and illustrations. In fact, for a general assessment of the state of conservation under the ASI today it should be enough to study carefully the photographs of the book. The illustrations, charts and tables fully complement the analytical work done by the audit team.

III. OBSERVATIONS

I must stress that this is the first document of its kind in the history of Indian archaeology. The ASI has been in existence since 1861 and this is for the first time that the scope of its work has been subject to close scrutiny by a government agency. There have been various committees in the past; in 2012-13 itself the Ministry of Education set up a three-member committee with the present author as Chairperson to assess the work of the then Director General, Dr. Gautam Sengupta. However, the reports submitted by such committees have not been published, and as the present report emphasizes, the recommendations of all these committees have by and large been ignored. Historically speaking it would be worthwhile to underline the fact that in the case of the 'expert committees' appointed by the Government of India to suggest improvements in the workings of the ASI, the experts themselves have by and large been somewhat half-hearted about the problems in hand. I remember that sometime during the NDA government under Shri Atal Bihari Vajpayee during his third term in the office (1999-2004) there was a committee to look into the affairs of the ASI with Shri B.B. Lal and Dr. S.P. Gupta among its members. I do not know what was suggested by this committee but Dr. Gupta told me that he was much impressed by the quality and variety of the breakfasts served by the ASI to its members! As far as the Wheeler committee is concerned, I know that Professor Nihar Ranjan Ray was one of its members. Ray was an art historian and did not have any grasp of Indian archaeological matters. He, in fact, failed miserably to give a positive shape to the Department of Archaeology, Calcutta University, during his deanship of this university's Faculty of Arts. The point is that 'committees' serve many purposes in the portals of bureaucracy and not many of them can be related to the basic task of professionally improving any government organization. The committee which formulated a research programme for the ASI on the Sarasvati river system lacked the necessary acumen to be able to contribute something significant to the problem.

In this whole range of generally mediocre reports drafted by people with half-hearted commitment to Archaeology in India, the present report towers significantly higher than the rest. Two of its features are particularly impressive: a close understanding of the entire structure of the organization it was assigned to investigate, and the details and the comprehensiveness of the points it was going to focus on. The structure of the report and the questions it asks itself are remarkably precise by any academic standard. Two more points need highlighting in this connection: the audit team was not composed of archaeologists and its work lasted for only about 10 months (from February 2012 to April 2013). The ease and competence with which this non-archaeological team pinpointed the basic structural nodes of the ASI with detailed critical evaluations commands nothing but praise and respect.

The major points of the report have been summarized above, and all that I propose to do here is to draw special attention to the points which I consider to be basic.

The report asserts (p. 221, paragraph 1) that the core function of the ASI relates to 'field archaeology that included excavation, survey and publication of excavation reports'. The fact that the audit team understands this point despite the fact that less than one per cent of the ASI budget is spent on its 'core function' should give proper archaeology students of the country almost a sense of relief. As non-archaeologists, the members of the audit team had no special reason to appreciate this point. In fact, right in the beginning of the report, they commit one of the two factual mistakes that one could detect in this volume: "the ASI, an attached office of the Ministry, was established in 1861 with the primary objective of conservation, preservation and maintenance of the centrally protected monuments" (p. 1). The second mistake they commit is in regard to the excavations at Bangarh: " Bangarh site was taken up for excavation in 2008-09, 70 years after its notification in 1938" (p. 104). Bangarh was, in fact, excavated for the first time in 1938-41, the excavations in 2008-09 being the second phase of excavations at the site.

Neither the ASI nor the Ministry of Culture, one of whose 'subordinate offices' the ASI is, seems to comprehend that the ASI was brought into existence in 1861 to research India's ancient archaeological past. The focus on conservation and preservation came somewhat later, being given firm official recognition only after the comprehensive formulation of the scope of archaeology in India by Lord Curzon as the Viceroy in 1901. The regrettable fact is that both the Ministry and the ASI now consider conservation to be their main, if not exclusive task. I drew attention to this point in connection with the appointment of Dr. Gautam Sengupta in 2010 as the first professional Director General of the ASI after 1993.

> The websites of the Ministry of Culture, Government of India, and one of its subordinate offices, the Archaeological Survey of India, cannot be accused of attaching any special significance to archaeological research. The 'mission statement' of the Ministry refers to only the "maintenance and conservation of heritage, historic sites and ancient monuments", and following this, the Archaeological Survey announces that the "maintenance of ancient monuments and archaeological sites and remains of national importance" is its "primary concern".
>
> From this official point of view, the Archaeological Survey of India is not a research or academic body. It is essentially a maintenance organisation on the model of the PWD.
>
> Whereas the PWD is concerned only with the construction and maintenance of modern structures, the Archaeological Survey of India's focus is on the maintenance and preservation of historic sites and monuments. We should soon get rid of the notion that the Archaeological Survey and its State level counterparts are supported by the Government to advance the academic cause of archaeology. After all, in very few countries of the modern world, the governments would take the direct responsibility of conducting archaeological research. That research has played only a minor part in the Archaeological Survey's post-Independence agenda is also clear from the sheer number of the unpublished explorations and excavations done by it.
>
> Secondly, when the advertisement came out (F.No-4-36/ 2009/ASI), the only firm requirement was that the

> aspiring candidates had served three years on a specified senior salary-scale. Otherwise, the net thrown was very wide: a post-graduate qualification (subject unspecified and no emphasis on the academic track record) and 15 years' experience in the fields of any of the following subjects: Archaeology, Architecture, Conservation, History, and Anthropology. Further, there had to be five years' experience (out of the specified fifteen years) in 'administration matters'. A bachelor's degree of Management was considered desirable. Apparently, the Ministry was not looking exclusively for a field archaeologist of proven brilliance to run its Archaeological Survey which, incidentally, is possibly the largest organisation of its kind in the world. In a sense, this lack of emphasis on research or even on Archaeology was not surprising. As noted earlier, the Ministry and the Survey both consider conservation to be their main task (Chakrabarti 2012, pp. 261-63).

The evidence is clear: archaeological research currently holds no place in the mind of either the ASI or the Ministry.

This has not happened in a day, and it is not easy to pinpoint the factors responsible for this state of affairs. To a great extent this is the result of the post of the DG going to the members of the Indian Administrative Service. The calibre of the individual officer varies but one has to admit that the Archaeological Survey of India was consistently made the happy hunting ground of a rather inferior group of people in the IAS which is still the premier bureaucratic set-up of the country. The Survey had uninterruptedly been under this bureaucratic control from 1993 to 2010, and that has certainly taken its toll. It is during this period that the ASI began to 'outsource' its work, which basically meant that the IAS Director Generals decided to pass on some work (and thus monetary benefit) to their favourite people outside the Survey. Whether these people were archaeologists or not did not really matter. Whether the self-styled conservation specialists of the INTACH or of the organizations which received the conservation contracts eventually changed the very character of the monuments they were supposed to conserve was of no concern to those in power in the country in these fields. It is only the contracts and the money which could be milked out of the Survey mattered. The new people who appeared in the scene and were close to the powers in the Ministry of Culture / the ASI or the political bigwigs of the Indian capital never had anything to do with archaeology, and thus archaeology slowly came to take a back seat in the whole ASI-Ministry structure.

The archaeologists of the 1970s and 1980s were no less responsible for damaging the official position of archaeology in the country. From 1977 to 1988, I was continuously based in Delhi and thus had a close opportunity to watch how the ASI of the period functioned. The Director Generals of the period had spent their lives before they became the DG, ASI, by doing archaeology in the field and were mostly financially honest on the personal level. But they could not prevent sloth and inertia from being firmly rooted in the Survey which had also become by then a nest of regionalism, casteism and corruption. They also could not prevent the external agency of the INTACH (Indian National Trust for Art and Cultural Heritage) from coming up in 1984 to compete with the ASI in the field of conservation. What the INTACH with its various centres throughout the country has done for the non-archaeological heritage of the country is of no concern to the Indian archaeologists, but as far as Indian archaeology is concerned, its contribution remains marginal. One DG ASI, Shri B.K.Thapar, became the Secretary of the INTACH after his retirement, thus setting a precedence in the matter of the retired ASI officers joining the INTACH.

Further, throughout the 1970s and 1980s, the ASI steadily lost interest in academic matters. The main reason for this was the increasing number of academically unmotivated people who found no merit in publishing the results of their field-work. Curiously enough, nobody has ever become penalized for not publishing their field-reports; non-publication was never a hindrance to their progress up the career ladder. There was also a rather rapid deterioration in the basic academic quality of the people recruited by the Survey. The brighter products of the Indian universities always found the ASI a tricky place to work in because the opportunities were better outside, but one must also admit that many of the new recruits of the 1970s and 1980s were students of very inferior quality. One of the background factors is that in the Indian university system, the study of ancient India in any form did not attract the bright students, and even in this situation somehow only the very bad among them got recruited to the ASI because of various non-academic considerations. Not much serious attempt was made to train the new recruits in the methodology and academics of archaeology as a discipline; the so-called Institute of Archaeology of the ASI taught virtually nothing seriously academic except giving hands-on experience in excavations and conservation. The academic aspects of archaeology still remain closed doors to most of the students of the ASI–run Institute of Archaeology.

To be fair to this institute, one must also admit that there has been by and large a remarkable deterioration in the quality of both teachers and students of ancient Indian history, culture and archaeology in Indian universities in recent years. The Ph.D.s in Ancient Indian History, Culture and Archaeology (AIHC and Archaeology) of most of these universities do not rise above the level of hopeless mediocrity, and one need not be surprised because their research supervisors also belong to the same level. An extraordinary large number of these Ph.D. students write their dissertations in mother-tongue and this generally means that they (and their teachers) are ignorant of the English language literature on their subject and are thus blissfully ignorant of the changing academic dynamics of the discipline. Even when there is familiarity with English, things may not be much better. Most of the Indian teachers of AIHC and Archaeology do not have any critical sense of either the theme or its 'sources' and have never been trained to write proper academic essays. They owe their university appointments generally to their personal political and personal network and they also expect their students and colleagues to be of the same low academic level. When H.D. Sankalia was important in the Deccan College (Pune), he used to say openly that he was not interested in having bright students as Ph.D. scholars because they would take up jobs and not complete their research. Even when the students seem to be promising in the light of their university mark-sheets, one has to be wary because good marks are given to the Indian university students not always on the basis of their actual performance. Again the issue of caste and political network comes in. The Ph.D. system of AIHC and Archaeology is seriously flawed. In most cases they are nothing but shoddy compilations of some data without any kind of originality. The Ph.D. examiners are selected from among the friends of the 'supervisor'. Nobody wants to upset a friend and virtually all who submit a Ph.D. thesis in AIHC and Archaeology are awarded the degree. I have to confess that as a Ph.D. examiner in my subject in many Indian universities, my role has been no less unpleasant. Whatever may be my personal opinion on the merit of a thesis, the student invariably gets his/her degree because I too do not want to upset my friend who put me in his/her examiner list. In a particular case, I decided that the thesis was too rubbishy to be put up for a degree, but the concerned supervisor reminded me that the candidate's marriage/job was at stake, and eventually I gave in. On the whole, this is a depressing scenario, and one does not really know how to get out of it.

The scenario is much more depressing than we think. The only professional Society which can be given the position of the major professional society of archaeologists in India is Indian Archaeological Society which has a large institutional campus in south Delhi. It never had any academic focus and the only concern of people at its helm has been to cling to their position as long as they can. For many years it has been nothing but an academic slum. The Society was set up in Banaras at the initiative of Professor A.K.Narain who was its first secretary. The journal *Puratattva* began to be published from Banaras. By the time of the sixth issue of *Puratattva* (1971-72), the Society came to Delhi with Shri B K Thapar of the ASI as its secretary. Then it came under the control of Dr. S.P.Gupta and the people of his personal network. The seed-money for the campus of the Society came from Professor Debahuti Singhal (Department of History, Delhi University) and her husband, Professor Damodar Singhal (Queensland University, Brisbane). Eventually the Society got a large parcel of land in the institutional area of Qutub Enclave in south Delhi, and now the Society is based in its own buildings in a well laid-out campus. The source of money for the imposing buildings is unclear, but Dr. S.P. Gupta was close to the RSS and it is probable that the building funds came from the RSS sources. Dr. Gupta himself donated the proceeds of the sale of his house in Delhi to the Society. The untimely death of the Singhal couple certainly robbed the Society of its academic focus. The subsequent leaders were never interested in anything beyond their own mediocrity and liked to be surrounded by hangers-on of various kinds, reducing the general ambience of the Society to that of an academic slum. The RSS patrons are not interested in its academic well-being.

Thus if the Ministry and the ASI are now silent in their websites about their responsibility of organizing and looking after archaeological research in the country, the situation is the inexorable product of many years of indifference to the academic health of the subject both in the ASI and the Departments of AIHC and Archaeology of the Indian universities.

The CAG report has also done a tremendous service to the cause of archaeology in India by drawing attention to the state of the epigraphy 'branch' of the Survey. In 2004, I had an opportunity to briefly visit the headquarter of this 'branch' in Mysore. The impression I got was that it was a hopelessly neglected institution sunk in despair. The CAG report has thrown light on its present condition with facts and figures which we here have summarized. There is a general sense of despondency all around, and this again is inexorably the product of many years of neglect of epigraphy both on the level of the Ministry and that of the Survey itself. One of the requisite qualifications on the Master's level to enter the ASI is Sanskrit, and nothing stands in the way of the young recruit to specialize in epigraphy and palaeography. That the young recruits avoid by and large to be specialists in this line is in a sense proved by the present sorry state of the Epigraphy Branch. The universities too, especially their Sanskrit departments, must be apportioned some blame for this development. Epigraphy and palaeography are generally taught as 'special papers' in the Sanskrit MA courses of many Indian universities, and if this could generate interest in palaeographical and epigraphical research, that would have been very fruitful. It must be remembered, however, that the status of Sanskrit in the intellectual firmament of the educated Indian middle class is very minor and anything related to Sanskrit (or Indian classics in general) is considered unworthy of proper respect and acceptance in the Indian market place.

The absence of any academic orientation chases us almost at every step. For many years the ASI has excavated sites without specific academic angles and by delaying their publications the ASI has also considerably diminished academic interests in them. The only field in which the ASI endeavour has been more or less successful in the recent years is the field of the Indus studies where excavations at Dholavira and a host of other sites including Rakhigarhi and Khirsara have significantly added to the general scholarly assessment of the Indus civilization. On the other hand, the lack of a definitive report (or even a brief monograph) on the Dholavira work has considerably downgraded the significance of this discovery which in a sense is more important than the discovery at Mohenjodaro. Among other things, the excavated remains at this place are better preserved and show the entire succession of continuous and interrelated chain of cultural developments right up to the end of the Indus civilization. The site, located in a well-defined island in the Rann of Kutch, also shows a very high technical level of water management. Thirdly, its division into 'castle-bailey', 'middle town' and 'lower town' and their separate fortifications have added a new perspective to the Indus town-planning. Although the excavations at the site have been put on hold for more than a decade, there has been no official interest in systematically exploring the environs of the site. The chain of large brick-built and occasionally rock-hewn reservoirs around the periphery of the site should have raised questions about the methods of water management by the ancient

Indus people in this part of Kutch. Regrettably this is still a closed chapter in detail. Innumerable examples of this kind may be given. No academic problem has been followed up systematically by the ASI for many years.

Regarding the antiquities in the possession of the ASI and the 'national level' museums, the report has continuously emphasized the significance of documenting them properly and digitising their records. This is an essential academic aspect of archaeological research. It is somewhat incredible that there is no national register of antiquities. It appears that after the CAG report was submitted the Ministry of Culture has eventually woken up to the idea. However, the way they are thinking of doing it—or have already decided upon the way to do it—is interesting from the national perspective and made clear by the following report in *The Hindu* of January 31, 2014. We reproduce below the whole news-item.

NEW PROJECT AIMS TO DIGITALLY CONNECT ALL NATIONAL MUSEUMS.

> Paintings, sculptures and other cultural treasures and artefacts at national and ASI museums across the country will now be made available digitally as part of a single, searchable database.
>
> All museums which are directly funded by the Centre along with the 44 site museums being run by Archaeological Survey of India have agreed to use a single database and taxonomic system to catalogue their collections, making India the first country to adopt such a nationwide system.
>
> The initiative is a result of the 'Vivekananda Memorial Programme for Museum Excellence' which the Art

> Institute of Chicago (AIC) and the Union Culture Ministry agreed to devise in 2012.
>
> "The major museums in the country have not digitised their collection. Information on various objects is not digitally available. That is where the software will be useful," National Museum Director General, Dr. Venu V, told PTI.
>
> The software has been developed by the Pune-based Centre for Development of Advanced Computing (C-DAC).
>
> "It will take at least two to three years to complete the entire project", Venu said.
>
> AIC President Douglas Druick said that his organisation has been working with various museums to encourage modern practices like conservation, planning of exhibitions, etc.
>
> "We had the AIC staff travel to India and conduct seminars on the theme of collection management and preventive conservation. We have also hosted officials from Indian museums in Chicago for seminars," Druick said. "The project has achieved measurable success and we are honoured to embark on such an extensive professional programme with support from the Indian government."

Among the museums set to be digitally connected are the National Museum (Delhi), Indian Museum and the Victoria Memorial Hall (both in Kolkata), Salarjung Museum (Hyderabad), Allahabad Museum and the National Gallery of Modern Art in Delhi, Bangalore and Mumbai.

Several of ASI's site museums, including those at Sarnath, Nagarjunakonda, Vikramshila, Old Goa, and Fort St. George, are also included.

The first question which comes to mind is: why India could not undertake the task herself, especially when the relevant software has been developed by C-DAC of Pune? Secondly, was it necessary to involve the Art Institute of Chicago in the organization of seminars 'on the theme of collection management and preventive conservation'. As far as one is aware, there are several 'museum studies' or museology departments in the Indian universities. Why could not they be given the responsibility of organizing such seminars? Thirdly, are we aware that by giving the responsibility of digitising our museum collections of antiquities to the Art Institute of Chicago we are handing over virtually the total control of our antiquities to this foreign agency? Who will put up the digitised antiquities on the web and will we be expected to pay for access to the relevant websites? Who will have control over these websites, the Government of India or the Art Institute of Chicago or both ? Another question which remains is: is this Institute doing it for money or for free ? Could not one of the IT organizations of the country be given the contract to do it ? And, if the Art Institute of Chicago is doing it for free, what is its interest ? The answer to this last question should be straightforward: to gain control to the entire antiquity collection in India. The foreign institutions like the Art Institute of Chicago are not known for their philanthropic attitude to the Third World antiquities. With the kind of people who currently adorn India's culture establishment, indifference to the nation's interest is possibly only to be expected.

The lack of records in almost everything related to archaeology and museums haunts us at every stage, and this has been brought out excellently well by the audit team. In fact, the question we ask in the end is: what has the ASI been doing then in all these years ? Keeping proper records of its activities is the most basic task of any organization worth the name. Is this the general feature of only archaeology and museum establishments in the country or is it present at every level ? While acting as a chairperson in a meeting of the West Bengal government archaeology advisory group, I wanted to know how many monuments were being protected by the State department of archaeology of West Bengal. There was no answer because no systematic record of the monuments protected by the State was available. I found the situation bizarre but having read the CAG report on the ASI, I now realize that the archaeology and museum people of the country who are supposed to look after some very important aspects of the country's past have no faith in properly recording whatever they have been doing. Among other things, this means a signal failure on the part of the leadership of this and other related organizations.

The absence of records may also have something sinister in the background. As I type this, somebody has sent me a news item of January/February 2014 in the Bengali newspaper *Bartaman*. Forty crores of rupees were sanctioned for the archaeology museum of the Government of West Bengal. The amount was sanctioned by the 12th Financial Commission in 1912. What has transpired is that a very large chunk of this money has been spent without keeping proper records. If my memory does not fail me, news items of this type have also appeared in connection with two other Kolkata heritage establishments: Indian Museum and Victoria Memorial Hall. The heritage business seems to be quite profitable to India's 'heritage experts'. Keeping records, of course, is anathema because if proper records are kept, responsibilities can be pinpointed.

A large section of the Report is devoted to the miscellaneous issues of conservation and preservation. One does not normally expect the academically bankrupt people of the Ministry, the ASI, the museums and the Indian Archaeological Society to do anything academically useful. However, we expected that they would perform their task of conservation and preservation, which the Ministry and the ASI claim to be their sole task, with some amount of planning, care and competence. The audit team has furnished enough data to dispel this notion. Shoddy planning and clumsy work have characterised the ASI's conservation and preservation endeavours almost at every step. One has merely to look at the illustrations provided by the audit team.

I have been somewhat amused by the failure of the so-called heritage experts to prepare acceptable Site Management Plans, etc. as preparatory to putting the relevant sites 'on the World Heritage Site list'. The names of these heritage experts have been mentioned by the audit team. My idea is that the responsibility should have been given to ASI's conservators of the old school: old-fashioned Conservation Assistants of the ASI would know more about a site than India's 'conservation architect' brigade. In the name of conserving and preserving a monument, this brigade is actually bringing about the death of the old and reasonably successful tradition of archaeological conservation in the country. The reconstruction of the Humayun Tomb complex in Delhi done with much fanfare is a recent example of this ongoing process. While conserving a monument you are not supposed to undertake extensive reconstructions by using new components and there is no reason why the monument should have a new look. As the audit team points out,

> The principles guiding the preservation and restoration of ancient buildings should be agreed and be laid down on an international basis, with each country being responsible for applying the framework of its own culture

> and traditions ... The ASI and the Ministry were found lacking in the areas of policy formulation, setting standards, monitoring and documentation of conservation works (p. 63).

Myriads of issues have been raised by the audit team. For instance, the team questioned the National Mission on Monuments and Antiquities principle of compiling the relevant data on the basis of the secondary sources. This principle has seriously harmed the credibility of the data being compiled. Six months in the field in each 'Circle' followed by six months of writing would have enabled any energetic team to complete its task, at least on the preliminary level. Again, this team could follow the same routine in the second year, by the end of which we would have got a current status report on the sites and monuments within the limits of that particular 'Circle'. More than 80 lakhs were spent (p. 32) merely on putting the NMMA office in place in Delhi. That amount would have satisfactorily completed the basic documentation work in a 'Circle'. The allotted budget of Rs. 90 crores is enough to complete the basic task of the Mission on the basis of primary documentation, and that too within a well-defined period. The calculation goes like this: three people in the team with a rented vehicle in the field; six such teams to cover all the 24 'Circles', spending 2 years in each Circle. Not more than 8 years should be needed to complete the task on the basis of the first-hand study of the monuments and sites.

This report is a magnificent analytical document of the state of affairs in Indian archaeology. Equally importantly, this tells us how the present archaeological and museum administration of the country is run. The fact which inexorably asserts itself is that currently it is in the hands of people who do not even know what is to be done. However, if the situation ever changes, this report will be essential for the new generation to form its own policy, principles and methods. From this point of view the importance of this report cannot be overemphasized. On a personal level, the only consolation I have received is that there are still people in the country who can think of, and prepare, such a report.

Index